paraclesis
Coming alongside others

Journeying Together

DAILY GUIDE

CWR

TREVOR J. PARTRIDGE

DAILY GUIDE

Journeying Together

NAME:_____

παρακλησις: The NAS New Testament Greek Lexicon Strong's: – number 3874 – Transliterated Word – **Paraklesis**.
Phonetic Spelling: par-ak-lay-sis
Definition: calling alongside, summons, esp. for help, imploration, supplication, entreaty, exhortation, encouragement, consolation, comfort, solace; that which affords comfort or refreshment (Luke 2:25; Rom. 12:8; 15:4; 2 Cor. 1:3–7; Phil. 2:1)

Paraclesis is the anglicised transliteration of the Greek word (from Latin and French). It is what is described in the New Testament as the 'one another' ministry.

Published 2016 by CWR, Waverley Abbey House, Waverley Lane, Farnham, Surrey, GU9 8EP, UK.

CWR is a Registered Charity – Number 294387 and a Limited Company registered in England – Registration Number 1990308.

For list of National Distributors, visit www.cwr.org.uk/distributors

Concept development, editing, design and production by CWR.

Printed by Linneygroup UK

ISBN: 978-1-78259-417-8

Contents

Introduction

The Paraclesis initiative is designed to help you and your church develop your understanding and ability to care for each other. These skills can then be taken into your community as an expression of the gospel of grace.

Paraclesis came out of my desire to establish a culture of care in my own church and community. Through my journey and struggle with cancer, I experienced the care of others coming alongside and journeying with me from their own experience of battling the disease. As Paul explains in 2 Corinthians 1:3–4, when God brings us alongside someone else in hard times, it is so we can be there for that person. This six-week series, Paraclesis: Journeying Together, introduces the tools and gives foundational guidance on how to apply this teaching to everyday life.

The term 'Paraclesis' is built around the Greek word 'Paraklesis' (parakleo, parakletos, paraklete), which is found over 140 times in the New Testament. It means 'one who comes alongside'. Para: 'to be with', 'alongside'; kaleo: 'to call' or 'to come'. Therefore, the anglicised, 'Paraclesis' literally means 'to come alongside someone; to help, entreat, give assistance, aid, care, comfort, support, console, direct, encourage'.

About the Daily Guide

This *Daily Guide* is part of the six-week Paraclesis: Journeying Together series. Through using this companion workbook over the next forty-two days, you will discover what Scripture says about journeying and caring, and learn how to have a greater impact on those you meet every day.

This workbook is divided into six weekly themes, which each focus on a different New Testament narrative:

1. Caring – The Good Samaritan (Luke 10:25–37)

2. Loving – The Feeding of the 5,000 (Mark 6:31–44)

3. Journeying – The Disciples on the Emmaus Road (Luke 24:13–35)

4. Living – The Man by the Pool of Bethesda (John 5:1–15)

5. Healing – The Woman in the Temple (Luke 13:10–17)

6. Connecting – The Man at the Gate Beautiful (Acts 3:1–10)

On the title page of each week, you will see these themes are accompanied with a short Bible verse that relates to it. These should help you focus on what the theme for each week is really about.

Each week is then broken down into Sundays, weekdays and Saturdays, which all contain different features:

SUNDAY

Day one of each week begins on a Sunday with a sermon outline. This is designed for you to work through during that day's sermon, encouraging you to engage further with what is being said. Key points will be flagged for you throughout these Sunday pages and there will be space to fill in the missing words as well as jot down other notes that are important to you.

MONDAY–FRIDAY

Daily verse

To get the best out of your daily study, look up the day's verse in your Bible and read the context. You will see that throughout this Daily Guide, different Bible translations have been used to give your reading some variety. Where a translation is not specified, the passage has been taken from the New King James Version (NKJV).

Quote of the day

These are pithy quotes from well-known commentators who have something valuable to say about the subject of the day. The quotes are not so much to feed your mind, but to ignite your soul, provoking you to action, so that, in the words of Jesus in the parable of the Good Samaritan, you will 'Go and do likewise' (Luke 10:37).

Memory verse for the week

Every week there is a new memory verse to learn, which features at the end of each weekday and Saturday. They have fill-in sections that change each day, so by the end of the week you should find that you will have committed an important piece of scripture to memory.

Daily journal

This section provides space for you to jot down any thoughts or ideas you have as you explore the weekly theme each day.

Tips for journeying together

These are practical thoughts or skills you can incorporate and practise at some point during the day to help you sharpen your ability to effectively come alongside others. Each week, tips are divided into a different sub-theme, covering an important aspect of coming alongside another person. These include: awareness, coming alongside, being a good listener, being an empathiser, choosing your words and being a reflector.

SATURDAY

Day seven of each week (which falls on a Saturday) is a chance to reflect on what you have focused on that week and to engage with the process of going and doing.

Review
These questions can be used to help personal reflection as well as initiate discussion (potentially within a small group setting).

Journeying together action plan
This space is the chance for you to identify who you have come alongside or who you aim to connect with in the following week. Try and choose one person from your church family and someone from your local community, eg a work colleague.

Prayer
Each week ends in prayer, where we can ask God to help us take forward what we have learnt. You can either pray these prayers, or use them as a springboard for your own meditation.

The gift of your journey

In order to help you to think through the gift of your journey, there is an exercise at the back of this *Daily Guide*, which will help you identify an overview of your journey's story. It can be completed during the third week when we look at journeying and connecting our journey to others. If completed at this point, when your group meets together, you can begin to share with each other significant life events and circumstances that have been part of each of your journeys.

Useful Resources

Alongside this *Daily Guide* there is also a wealth of resources for you and your church to use to help you on your journey of coming alongside others. These include sermon notes, small group studies, leaders' guides, videos, daily acts of kindness, wristbands and journey cards for you to complete at the end of the series. For more information and to access, visit **www.paraclesis.org.uk**

If you would like to read more about Paraclesis, the companion book *Love With Skin On* further explores this idea, and takes you through the journey that led to the creation of this initiative.*

Journeying Together

Throughout the following six weeks (and beyond!), remember that we were not intended to live our lives alone, or 'on an island', but to journey alongside other people and with God. Whether within our family, church, work, community, or life in general, God uses us in other people's lives to impact each other.

*For more information and to order *Love With Skin On*, visit **www.cwr.org.uk**

Caring

'be ... compassionate, loving ...
tenderhearted' (1 Pet. 3:8, ASV)

SUNDAY

Who Cares?

The Good Samaritan – Luke 10:25–37

The journey called 'life'

'A certain man *went down from Jerusalem to Jericho'*
(Luke 10:30)

The priest and Levite were indifferent and _____
(vv31–32)

The Samaritan had _____ and concern
(vv33–34)

PARAKALEO – TO COME ALONGSIDE

*'All praise to the God and Father of our Master, Jesus the
Messiah! Father of all mercy! God of all healing counsel
[***paraklesis***]! He comes alongside us [***parakaleo***] when
we go through hard times, and before you know it, He
brings us alongside [***parakaleo***] someone else who is going
through hard times so that we can* **be there for that person**
*[***paraklesis***] just as God was there for us [***parakaleo***].'*
(2 Cor. 1:3–4, *The Message***, author's own emphasis)**

> **PARACLESIS: Coming alongside and being there for
> someone, to give help, aid, assistance, support and care.**

Developing the core value of care

The antithesis of paraclesis is _____ living
(1 Cor. 10:24, GNB)

Paraclesis is _____ living (Gal. 5:14)

'Love never gives up. Love cares more for others than for self.'
(1 Cor. 13:4, *The Message*)

Developing _____ of other people's needs

Recognising people _____ more than we
realise

PARAKALEO – TO ENCOURAGE

'encourage [**parakaleo**] one another **daily**, as long as it is
called "Today"' **(Heb. 3:13, NIV, author's own emphasis)**

**ENCOURAGEMENT: The expression of affirmation, verbally,
non-verbally or practically, giving support and inspiration
to someone on their journey, lifting them up, helping them to
overcome a difficult time.**

Be willing to:

- Move out of your _____ zone

- Become a _____ not a _____

- Focus on how much God _____

- Be alert for _____

- Learn to be a good _____

- Use _____ words

- Do acts of _____

Facing our core value of self-protection

Will we be like the priest and the Levite? Or will we be like the Samaritan? He could have stayed behind his barrier of self-protection, fearing rejection or unacceptance. But refusing to hide, he stepped out of his comfort zone, reached out, _____ and _____ with the man in need, taking care of him and fulfilling the _____ ministry.

Jesus' challenge to the lawyer, and to us too, is: _____ (Luke 10:37)

Sermon Notes

The Interests of Others

*'Those of us who are strong and able in the faith need to step
in and lend a hand to those who falter, and not just do what
is most convenient for us. Strength is for service, not status.
Each one of us needs to look after the good of the people
around us, asking ourselves, "How can I help?"'*
(Rom. 15:1–2, *The Message*)

In response to the lawyer's question, 'And who is my neighbour?'
(Luke 10:29), Jesus answered that every person in need is our neighbour.
He taught this through the parable of the Good Samaritan, describing
the plight of a man on a journey. As this man travelled, life circumstances
unexpectedly overtook him and he was attacked by robbers. Two people
of 'faith' then came by (possibly coming from, or heading towards,
church) and observed their neighbour in need. It is possible that the priest
may have said to himself, 'I'm a priest, not a paramedic,' and the Levite,
following hard on his heels, may have thought 'I'm a Levite, not a social
worker,' so they both walked by the hurting man.

We often like to make these two people out to be the bad guys, but I
don't necessarily think they were – the robbers are the villains of this
story. These were the *busy* guys – busy working for God, but too busy
to be concerned about a beaten-up man in need on the side of the road.
Maybe they were just too caught up in and absorbed with the importance
and demands of their own busy religious world? Their busyness and self-
absorption did not necessarily make them bad people, but bad neighbours.

The question to ask ourselves is this: does this attitude depict the Church of
today? Writing to the Corinthians, Paul said 'None of you should be looking
out for your own interests, but for the interests of others' (1 Cor. 10:24,
GNB). This message can sound counter-intuitive to us today. Our culture that
often glorifies self-sufficiency and self-reliance, and admires independent,
self-fulfilled living, can seem to promote a way of life that makes the
individual supreme and sovereign over everything.

The challenge then is this: will we let our own personal interests take precedence over the interests of others and, like the priest and the Levite, find we've become too busy, self-absorbed and preoccupied? Or will we choose to become more 'neighbour-conscious' and 'other-focused', recognising that crossing over the road to engage with a neighbour in need requires denying the very self we may have for so long served?

I once heard that a good test of 'other-centredness' is whether or not you let others go first at the checkout line, the give way sign or when you are queuing generally. Writing to the Philippians, Paul encourages, 'Don't let selfishness and prideful agendas take over. Embrace true humility, and lift your heads to extend love to others. Get beyond yourselves and protecting your own interests; *be sincere*, and secure your neighbors' interests first. *In other words*, adopt the mind-set of Jesus the Anointed. *Live with His attitude in your hearts.*' (Phil. 2:3–5, TV).

Quote of the day

'The first question that the priest and the Levite asked was "If I stop to help this man, what will happen to me?"' But then the Good Samaritan came by and he reversed the question, "If I do not stop and help this man, what will happen to him?"' [1]
– Martin Luther King Jr

Memory verse for the week

'A _____ command I give you: love one another. As I have loved you, so you must love one another.' (John 13:34, NIV)

Daily Journal

_____

_____

_____

_____

_____

_____

_____

_____

_____

_____

_____

_____

_____

_____

_____

_____

_____

_____

Tips for journeying together: Awareness
When considering your awareness of someone you wish to
come alongside, one expression of encouragement is to give
that person your complete undivided attention. Attention
conveys acceptance and assurance. Cultivate awareness by
totally focusing on the person you are talking with, giving
them your full concentration, not showing distraction or
disinterest.

A Core Value

*'[Jesus said] "Self-help is no help at all. Self-sacrifice is the
way, my way, to finding yourself, your true self."'*
(Matt. 16:25, *The Message*)

When we accept Christ, we no longer have the assignment of looking out
for our own interests; our job becomes representing the interests of Jesus
Christ who, like the Samaritan, was other-centred. Like it or not, it's not all
about us.

Yesterday we saw that every day we can be encouraged and influenced
towards living a self-centred life, focused on our own interests. In Jesus'
parable, the Samaritan understood what the priest and Levite failed to. He
was willing to 'come alongside' the stricken man, then 'journey together'
with him to the inn and take care of him. Caring for this person in need was
a core value to the Samaritan. The Samaritan overcame his fears, stepped
outside of himself and his comfort zone, and took the risk to cross the road.

This story is an intriguing model of altruistic motivation, altruism being
unconcern for our own wellbeing because of an enduring concern for the
wellbeing of others. In this sense, altruism requires a change of perspective
and attitude, fully embracing the Christ life. It is through Jesus and His power
at work within us that we find strength to put the needs of others first.

An article titled, 'How to be Miserable' explains that all you need to do to
feel this way is:

> *'Think about yourself. Talk about yourself. Use "I" as often
> as possible. Mirror yourself continually in the opinion of
> others. Listen greedily to what people say about you. Expect
> to be appreciated. Be suspicious. Be jealous and envious. Be
> sensitive to slights. Never forgive a criticism. Trust nobody
> but yourself. Insist on consideration and respect. Demand
> agreement with your own views on everything. Sulk if people
> are not grateful to you for favours shown them. Never forget a
> service you have rendered. Do as little as possible for others.'* [2]

Ask yourself these questions: Can I let someone else tell their story without interrupting them with my own? Can I let someone else choose where we go? Can I let others take the credit? Can I be genuinely happy for others' success? Am I always competing with others for attention? Do I always turn the conversation back to me?

It's amazing how, when we are willing to reach outside of ourselves to others and care for them, we become less and less concerned and absorbed with being the centre of our own universe, and less and less prone to personal angst. When we choose the way of 'self-sacrifice' – overcoming our own fears of inadequacy – then in the words of our Bible verse today, 'we find ourselves, our true self'. We overcome the barriers that make us think that being a neighbour has too much risk or is too costly, or that we don't have the time or resources to get involved. Recognise today that, in Christ, your limitations are not greater than His resources. The apostle Paul said, 'Love never gives up. Love cares more for others than for self' (1 Cor. 13:4, *The Message*).

Quote of the day

'God sends no one away empty except those who are full of themselves.'[3]– Dwight L. Moody

Memory verse for the week

'A new _____ I give you: love one another. As I have loved you, so you must love one another.' (John 13:34, NIV)

Daily Journal

_____

_____

_____

_____

_____

_____

_____

_____

_____

_____

_____

_____

_____

_____

_____

_____

_____

_____

Tips for journeying together: Awareness

Experts tell us, communication that encourages falls into
three categories: the words we use, how warm our tone
of voice is and whether we use attentive, non-verbal body
language. An encourager makes sure all three complement
each other and does not convey contradictory messages.

WEDNESDAY

The Root of Uncaring

'Never tell your neighbors to wait until tomorrow if you can help them now.' **(Prov. 3:28, GNB)**

I think the priest and Levite somehow missed today's verse when they were reading the wisdom literature of the Old Testament. It must have inadvertently escaped their attention. We are beginning to see that one of the reasons why we may often be uncaring is our preoccupation with our own self-centred lifestyles. It could be because of this that we miss the daily opportunities to help others. God is constantly placing people in our path, but because our eyes can be so self-focused, we fail to fully recognise the needs of others. We suffer from spiritual myopia, commonly known as near-sightedness, a condition of the eye, which fails to clearly see distant objects.

Egocentricity is the state of being selfishly, solely concerned with our own desires, needs and interests, acting out of the distorted view that the self is all-important, even to the detriment of those around us. In Greek mythology, Narcissus saw his reflection in a pool and became so absorbed that he fell in love with it, not realising it was an image of his own reflection. Besotted and captivated by himself, he was unable to leave his own reflection and died alone by the pool. It is from him we get the word 'narcissist'.

A doctor once said, 'Every self-centred person draws disease to himself like a magnet draws iron filings.' He cited the case of an over-privileged, over-indulged girl. Everything had to centre on her. She had everything thrown into her lap – money, opportunity, a good education, prestige and so on, but she was so self-centred that she couldn't enjoy anything. Every sickness that came into the neighbourhood affected her. 'That,' said the doctor, 'is the end of egocentrics. They start out to draw life to themselves – its joys, its thrills – and all they succeed in drawing to themselves is sadness, disillusionment and sickness, spiritual, mental and physical.'[4]

Egocentricity also takes away our awareness of others, and desensitises us to the need of the moment. Today's verse reminds us that the best time to give help is in the here and now, not some other time. We do not know how long the opportunity will last; there is no guarantee of tomorrow. For the priest and Levite, the opportunity to help the wounded man was lost.

Egocentric behaviour ignores the needs of others, and neglects taking the time needed to understand or even consider another person's point of view and feelings. Giving consideration to others around us and preferring one another is something we need to continually work on. Paul encourages this, writing, 'Instead of being motivated by selfish ambition or vanity, each of you should, in humility, be moved to treat one another as more important than yourself' (Phil. 2:3, NET). Ultimately, egocentricity is self-destructive because it takes our time and attention away from God and from the opportunities He places before us.

Quote of the day
'Come over here and sit next to me, I'm dying to tell you all about myself.'[5] – Unknown

Memory verse for the week

'A new command _____ _____ _____:

love one another. As I have loved you, so you must

love one another.' (John 13:34, NIV)

Daily Journal

_____

_____

_____

_____

_____

_____

_____

_____

_____

_____

_____

_____

_____

_____

_____

_____

_____

_____

_____

Tips for journeying together: Awareness
Our body language accounts for 55% of our communication.
Awareness of our gestures, expressions, posture etc is
important. Ask someone to feed back to you about the effects
of the non-verbal signals you send out.

Let's Get Real!

*'[Jesus said] "You can't keep your true self hidden forever;
before long you'll be exposed. You can't hide behind a
religious mask forever; sooner or later the mask will slip and
your true face will be known."'* **(Luke 12:2, *The Message*)**

As this week progresses, I hope you are coming to the realisation that
we were created by God to be caring and concerned people, to come
alongside others, and that if we abandon this divine design we will
probably live impoverished, self-centred lives. One of the greatest
reasons that prevent us from reaching out to others is the fear of rejection
and unacceptance.

Fear of rejection and failure causes many people never to start or try
anything that is not completely safe or risk-free. It prevents us from
doing anything that might receive criticism, ridicule or humiliation. The
Samaritan in Jesus' parable knew rejection and unacceptance. He was
regarded as a heretic, a religious outcast. Yet he was willing to face his
own fear of rejection and unacceptability and was moved with compassion
to step out of his comfort zone, facing his own fear of rejection, to journey
with someone in need.

Nevertheless, even when we know we should not be afraid, it is still
tempting to hide. John Powell's book *Why Am I Afraid to Tell You Who I Am?*
explains, 'I am afraid to tell you who I am because if I tell you who I am, you
might not like who I am, and that is all I have to give.'[6]

Perhaps it is a shared belief like this that makes us long for acceptance and
dread rejection. As our Bible passage for today puts it, we become adept
at 'hiding behind masks' to keep our real self hidden from view. We can
often feel that the fear of exposing our own needs becomes one of the
most discouraging and debilitating factors preventing us from meeting the
needs of others.

There is a popular view that says you need to:

- Know yourself

- Accept yourself

- Express yourself

How can we know ourselves unless we know who we are in Christ? As a child of God, made in His likeness, created in His image, we can only truly know our self as we know Him. How is it possible to accept ourselves outside of Christ as unredeemed sinners, unacceptable to ourselves and others? Only when a person has been changed by Christ are they truly able to accept themselves in Him. Outside of Christ, what kind of self can a person express? As our verses say today, you can't keep your true self hidden forever; before long you'll be exposed.

There was a time when we were unacceptable in God's sight because of our sin, guilt and shame, but now through forgiveness and salvation we are accepted in Christ. Ephesians 1:6 puts it like this, 'He made us accepted in the Beloved'. What a glorious truth and reality! We are not just made acceptable, but we have been accepted in Christ, and given the same standing as our Saviour. Even though there are things about yourself you find hard to accept, and things about you that others may find hard to accept, stop putting yourself and others down, and believe the promise that you are accepted in the Beloved.

Quote of the day
'Never build a wall until you know what you are walling in – and what you are walling out.'[7] – John Powell

Memory verse for the week
'A new command I give you: _____

_____ _____.

As I have loved you, so you must love one another.' (John 13:34, NIV)

Daily Journal

_____

_____

_____

_____

_____

_____

_____

_____

_____

_____

_____

_____

_____

_____

_____

_____

_____

_____

_____

Tips for journeying together: Awareness
As well as their personal space, be aware of other people's
psychological space. Don't try and get too close to them
through overcrowding or overwhelming them with gushing
enthusiasm, inappropriate hugs or bone-crushing handshakes.
Try to be warm and considerate, gentle and pleasant.

FRIDAY

It's Down to You

'This is how we've come to understand and experience love: Christ sacrificed his life for us. This is why we ought to live sacrificially for our fellow believers, and not just be out for ourselves.' **(1 John 3:16, *The Message*)**

As we have seen from this week's parable, the priest and the Levite were self-centred, but the Samaritan was other-centred. After He told the parable, Jesus asked the lawyer 'So which of these three do you think was neighbor to him who fell among the thieves?' and the man replied, 'He who showed mercy on him' (Luke 10:36–37).

Being self-centred prevents us from being other-centred. This begs the question: how do we move from being self-centred to other-centred? The Christian faith offers only one way, the way of self-surrender. Paul puts it succinctly in Galatians 2:20 (NASB): 'I have been crucified with Christ; and it is no longer I who live, but Christ lives in me'. This is the good news of the gospel, that one of the most significant outcomes of Christ's atonement is to deliver us from the very self we have served for so long. This is the journey we are on. It commenced when we first surrendered our lives at the cross, when He came alongside, and we received forgiveness and found new life in Christ. At the cross, the big 'I' (the centre of sin, guilt and pride) was crucified, alongside Christ, in a moment of profound surrender. I wonder whether you have experienced the liberating power of the cross in relation to self-centredness? Through redemption, we are not only saved from sin, but we are saved from ourselves. This truly is good news!

The principle of self-surrender is this – the self, or ego, is offered up lovingly as Jesus offered Himself up on that cross. You can't really selflessly care for others until the very self you have served has been put properly in its place – into the hands of Christ. Yourself in your own hands is the problem – yourself in the hands of Christ is the solution.

So come again and stand before the cross of Christ, gaze upward into the loving face of our Saviour and surrender yourself to Him afresh.

See how His sacrificial, suffering love has taken your place and mine. Lift your ego to Him today in full surrender for cleansing and redirection and walk away from the cross, free from self-interest, re-energised in His love and compassion. Because of His great love for us, we can withhold nothing from Him – not even our very self. Now we are free to serve others in His name.

Let's read that verse again: 'This is how we've come to understand and experience love: Christ sacrificed his life for us. This is why we ought to live sacrificially for our fellow believers, and not just be out for ourselves' (1 John 3:16, *The Message*).

Quote of the day
'God had brought me to my knees and made me acknowledge my own nothingness, and out of that knowledge I had been reborn. I was no longer the centre of my life and therefore I could see God in everything.'[8] – Bede Griffiths

Memory verse for the week
'A new command I give you: love one another.

As _____ _____ _____

_____, so you must love one another.'

(John 13:34, NIV)

Daily Journal

_____

_____

_____

_____

_____

_____

_____

_____

_____

_____

_____

_____

_____

_____

_____

_____

_____

_____

Tips for journeying together: Awareness

Eye contact is important when coming alongside someone
to encourage and support. Be careful not to stare at people
when trying to get a point across, or avoiding eye contact
when they are talking to you. A good rule is: when they talk,
hold their gaze gently, but when you talk, look away from time
to time.

Review

Think back over this week, the sermon content, the daily readings and the memory verse. You could read your Daily Journal entries to refresh your memory of each day. Now jot down one or more comments under the questions below:

· What more have I learnt about God this week?

· What have I learnt about others this week?

· What have I learnt about myself this week?

JOURNEYING TOGETHER ACTION PLAN

In the light of what you have learnt during this first week, write down the names of two people who you can start to connect with in a meaningful way during the next week. If you do not know their name yet, think of a way to ask and then intentionally plan to get alongside them.

- Church family:

  _____

- Local community/work colleagues:

  _____

Prayer
Lord, I have been challenged and inspired by Your account of the Good Samaritan. Give me courage and strength to follow Your clear instruction to 'Go and do likewise'. Amen.

Memory verse for the week

'A new command I give you: love one another. As I have loved you, so you must _____

_____ _____.'

(John 13:34, NIV)

Loving

'If I ... don't love, I'm nothing ... Love never gives up. Love cares more for others than for self. Love ... Isn't always "me first" ... Always looks for the best, Never looks back, But keeps going to the end. Love never dies.' (1 Cor. 13:2–8, *The Message*)

Love Comes Alongside

The Feeding of the 5,000 – Mark 6:31–44

We all go through hard times

'He comes alongside us when we go through hard times, and before you know it, he brings us alongside someone else who is going through hard times so that we can be there for that person just as God was there for us.' **(2 Cor. 1:4, *The Message*)**

1. **God comes alongside us**

2. **God brings us alongside someone else**

A paraclesis culture in our church

'let us not give up meeting together. Some are in the habit of doing this. Instead, let us encourage [**parakaleo**] one another with words of hope. Let us do this even more as you see Christ's return approaching' **(Heb. 10:25, NIRV)**

PARAKLESIS ETHOS – CULTURE

> CULTURE: Creating an environment in which we intentionally and regularly come alongside others, with support and help.

How can we begin to grow this culture of care within our church?

> *'When we have the opportunity to help anyone, we should do it. But we should give special attention to those who are in the family of believers.'* **(Gal. 6:10, NCV)**

Create the _____ to establish culture
(Gal. 6:10)

Consider _____ we can come alongside
(Heb. 10:24)

_____ to come alongside (Heb. 10:25)

Coming alongside means:

- Recognising that people do not have problems but _____

- Knowing how to receive and _____ love

- Loving as we have been _____ by God

- An expression of _____ community

> *'we are anxious that you keep right on loving others as long as life lasts'* **(Heb. 6:11, TLB)**

The heart of a paraclesis culture

The disciples suffered from:

Compassion _____ _____

> *'If you see some brother or sister in need and have the means to do something about it but turn a cold shoulder and do nothing, what happens to God's love? It disappears. And you made it disappear.'* **(1 John 3:17, *The Message*)**

'Jesus, when He came out, saw a great multitude and was moved with compassion for them, because they were like sheep not having a shepherd.' **(Mark 6:34)**

In contrast to this lack of compassion, Jesus had **a caring and compassionate ethos**

He _____ them

He _____ them

He _____ to them

> **COMPASSION: Moved inwardly to get involved, care and come alongside.**

Mark 6:34–44 shows us that compassion:

- Moves towards others

- Accepts responsibility for others

- Gives no excuses

- Places what we have in Jesus' hands

- Draws on Christ's resources

- Reaches out to the point of felt need

- Demonstrates *love coming alongside*

Sermon Notes

Becoming Alongsiders

'By this everyone will know that you are My disciples, if you have love and unselfish concern for one another.'
(John 13:35, AMP)

Last week, we saw how the Good Samaritan *came alongside* the stricken man, tended to him, then *journeyed* with him to an inn to take care of him. This week, we are going to look at Jesus after a busy day of non-stop ministry as He headed across Lake Galilee for some quiet time with the disciples.

This episode happened right after John the Baptist's death (Matt. 14), when Jesus was grieving deeply for His cousin. If anyone had a right not to engage with 'gate-crashing' church-goers, it was Jesus on this occasion. To His disciples, the crowd was a problem to be sent home, but to Jesus, they were hungry, weary and unloved. His heart was to get alongside them, to love them and meet their need in the context of 'doing church' together.

Our text today underlines that before we can effectively impact the world by telling everyone that God loves and cares for them, when it comes to the gospel, demonstration must precede proclamation. The fact of the matter is that we often affect others more by what we do than what we say. As the old adage says, 'actions speak louder than words'. Before the Church can effectively communicate the gospel to the world, it must first evidence it by coming alongside with compassion and love.

If the gospel is not seen in the community-life of the Church, and all we have to offer is empty rhetoric rather than delivering something of substance, then people tend to be dismissive of the seriousness of our message. But if what we say is backed up by a caring and compassionate lifestyle of loving and supporting one another, then the message is singularly authentic and attractive. If the wider secular community witness a strong culture of care, and joyous Christian neighbours, they will be drawn towards it by its sheer attractiveness and strength.

The world will not judge us by the amount of church activities or services we hold, but by the consistency of our deeds with our doctrine. It's not good enough simply proclaiming the virtues of our beliefs without down-to-earth evidence that we mean what we say. Or, as I once heard, 'if you walk the walk ... talk ain't necessary'. If we only talk a good game, but do little to achieve a result, then our claims are hollow. Let's put some legs to our words, stop talking and start doing!

One of the biggest deterrents to people coming to Christ is not a lack of evangelism, but a lack of demonstrable care and compassion. Remember, Jesus gave the world the right to judge the authenticity of our faith by how we come alongside one another (John 13:35). The proof of discipleship is not necessarily our love for Jesus, but our love for one another. The world listens when Christians love. One might say that love is the badge of our discipleship, the irrefutable evidence that convinces the world.

Quote of the day

'Preach the gospel always, and if necessary use words.' [1]
– St Francis of Assisi

Memory verse for the week

'that there _____ be no division in the body, but that the members may have the same care for one another.' (1 Cor. 12:25, ESV)

Daily Journal

WEEK 2
LOVING

_____

_____

_____

_____

_____

_____

_____

_____

_____

_____

_____

_____

_____

_____

_____

_____

_____

_____

Tips for journeying together: Coming alongside
Today, stop what you are doing and think of someone you
know at church. Pray for them, perhaps telephone them, send
a note of encouragement or even visit their home to let them
know you are thinking of them.

Front Door or Back Door?

'Right now, therefore, every time we get the chance, let us work for the benefit of all, starting with the people closest to us in the community of faith.' **(Gal. 6:10, *The Message*)**

There is no question, we have a responsibility to reach out and come alongside all who find themselves in need. However, sometimes the focus on outward evangelistic outreach to the local community is such that we overlook the immediate needs of those among us. Many churches suffer from the 'front door, back door' syndrome. They are so busy concentrating their efforts on getting new people through the front door that they fail to recognise the current members of the congregation who are rapidly slipping through the back door.

In asking people over many years why they left a particular church, the vast majority have told me it was because they felt uncared for or unappreciated. No one really got alongside them and cared. How sad. Researchers in this area say that the biggest factors for the 'front door, back door' syndrome are the lack of close, caring relationships, and the lack of a meaningful service. They say that it takes a person about four weeks to move from 'I don't *think* this church cares about me' to 'I *know* that this church doesn't care about me'.

So, on this matter of care, do we equally concern ourselves with both the people who already come to our church and our community? Our text today seems to put this clearly into context. The ERV translation says, 'When we have the opportunity to do good to anyone, we should do it. But we should give special attention to those who are in the family of believers' (Gal. 6:10). While we must have genuine concern for everyone, taking every opportunity to help, we are also to give special attention to coming alongside those in our community of faith.

A long-held view has been that the prime task of the Church is to reach out to people who are not believers first to get them into heaven, as ailing believers will make it anyway. But this is a very short-sighted view, as it actually creates not just a 'front door, back door' syndrome, but a 'revolving door' one too. As soon as people come in, they see we don't really know how to come alongside and care for each other, never mind care for them, and leave the same way they entered. How can we say we care for everyone if we don't take time to come alongside those who are part of the family of God? Could it be that we fail to make a deep impression on the non-Christian community because the Church itself is failing at this important truth of paraclesis, which is to effectively care for our own?

A church caretaker was once collecting sweet wrappers from the floor after the service, when he found a note from a well-known verse, written by an anonymous poet. It read, 'To dwell above with the Saints we love, Oh that will be glory, But to dwell below with the Saints we know, That's another story.'

Quote of the day
'Without a sense of caring, there can be no sense of community'[2]
– Anthony J. D'Angelo

Memory verse for the week

'that there may be no _____ in the body, but that the members may have the same care for one another.' (1 Cor. 12:25, ESV)

Daily Journal

_____

_____

_____

_____

_____

_____

_____

_____

_____

_____

_____

_____

_____

_____

_____

_____

Tips for journeying together: Coming alongside

When we judge someone with our words, it isolates them.
When we use words, they should neither condemn nor
condone. When you come alongside someone, remember that
we have all sinned and fallen short of God's glory, and so we can
give everyone a fair hearing in the light of both grace and truth.

Lives Singing in Harmony

'May our dependably steady and warmly personal God develop maturity in you so that you get along with each other as well as Jesus gets along with us all. Then we'll be a choir – not our voices only, but our very lives singing in harmony in a stunning anthem to the God and Father of our Master Jesus!'
(Rom. 15:5–6, *The Message*)

I sat at my desk one day and took a call from a businessman who was passing through London Heathrow airport from the USA. Someone had given him my name and phone number, telling him I could be of help. When I arrived at his hotel near the airport, he poured the problems of his life out to me. After a couple of hours with him, I suggested that when he returned from his business trip, he connect to a local church. 'Well,' he said, 'there's another part of the problem. Someone also told me to go to church and I did just that, but after three weeks it was clear that the church was in the middle of a major fight, and, although a new attendee, people were trying to pull me in both directions. I had enough and never returned.' What did I learn from this businessman? Most people don't reject God, they reject the church. John says, 'if we say we love God and don't love each other, we are liars. We cannot see God. So how can we love God, if we don't love the people we can see?' (1 John 4:20, CEV).

Someone has described these kind of churches as 'cannibal Christians'. J.B. Phillips translates Galatians 5:15 like this: 'But if freedom means merely that you are free to attack and tear each other to pieces, be careful that it doesn't mean that between you, you destroy your fellowship altogether!' Of course, the Christian community is not perfect. It is full of people with hurts, habits and hang-ups – that's life – but its dynamic and genius is that, with Christ at work in each of us, we can come alongside one another and love, care, share and grow together. Paul puts it like this: 'So let's agree to use all our energy in getting along with each other. Help others with encouraging words; don't drag them down by finding fault' (Rom. 14:19, *The Message*). So there it is. We can all be part of the paraclesis ministry.

Our text today says we can 'be a choir – not our voices only, but our very lives singing in harmony in a stunning anthem to the God and Father of our Master Jesus'. As we encourage and get alongside each other, the lyrics of our message will be backed by the harmony of the music we are playing together. What is the music of the gospel? It is the symphony of transformed lives and relationships through the power of the risen Christ at work amongst us, bringing us together in unity. In a discordant world, the miraculous music of redeeming and transforming grace needs to be heard loud and clear.

Authentic Christian community continues to be a loving, caring, healthy fellowship no matter how rough it gets, so that its message to the world carries maximum effectiveness and impact. 'But, dear brothers, I beg you in the name of the Lord Jesus Christ to stop arguing among yourselves. Let there be real harmony so that there won't be splits in the church. I plead with you to be of one mind, united in thought and purpose' (1 Cor. 1:10, TLB).

Quote of the day
'A man is called selfish not for pursuing his own good, but for neglecting his neighbour's.'[3] – Richard Whately

Memory verse for the week
'that there may be no division in the _____, but that the members may have the same care for one another.'
(1 Cor. 12:25, ESV)

Daily Journal

_____

_____

_____

_____

_____

_____

_____

_____

_____

_____

_____

_____

_____

_____

_____

_____

_____

Tips for journeying together: Coming alongside
Watch out for any mannerisms you may have developed that
could be seen as irritating to others, eg cracking your knuckles
etc. You may not be aware of these quirks, and they may not
seem much to you, but they may be distracting to someone
else who is trying to confide in you.

Quadraphonic Saints

'If you see some brother or sister in need and have the means to do something about it but turn a cold shoulder and do nothing, what happens to God's love? It disappears. And you made it disappear. My dear children, let's not just talk about love; let's practice real love. This is the only way we'll know we're living truly, living in God's reality.' **(1 John 3:16–18, *The Message*)**

Today, let's address how we can best fulfil the words in today's reading. How can we not just talk about love but also *practice* real love and care for one another by showing practical concern for people? How can we come alongside each other, loving each other the way God loves us? As we read the following suggestions, I think it is important to remember that, although the disciples may be seen to be problem-orientated, Jesus was always people-focused.

SEE PEOPLE AS PEOPLE WITH REAL NEEDS

Real needs require real help, and real help is hands-on. Jesus came alongside real people, encountering them face-to-face in the real situations of life. In an age when impersonal contact such as email, Twitter, smartphone, texting, Facebook and other social networks are often the order of the day, let's not lose the value of personal contact! Although these technological methods can be good for keeping in touch with people, especially if they live far away, whatever your environment is, the *best* kind of connection is by getting alongside others with personal contact, not just sitting in front of a screen, phone or desk. Jesus didn't email or text the woman at the well, He came alongside her and sat with her by the well. Sometimes we get so caught up in the modern era with all of its trappings that we forget the basic and simple elements of life. What better place than at church to make that individual connection, the personal touch that simply says, 'I care about you, I'll come and sit by your "well" with you'. 'Get along with each other; don't be stuck-up. Make friends with nobodies; don't be the great somebody' (Rom. 12:14–16, *The Message*).

HAVE A CARING ATTITUDE

Coming alongside others is more than just caring when we feel like it. It is an attitude of mind and heart that applies itself to doing what God expects of us, whether we feel like it or not. When we know the right thing to do, even though we may not feel like doing it, then doing it is an act of love. This is not to say that feelings should not be involved, but if we wait for feelings, they may arrive too late. A person with a caring attitude takes action whether feelings are there or not.

HEAR A PERSON'S HEART

We need to recognise that a person's words are like smoke from a simmering volcano, often loaded with emotion, anger, disappointment, guilt, sadness and bitterness. Take time to come alongside and tune in to what lies beneath what people are expressing – their deeper needs – as well as hear their point of view. Often, we are so busy and preoccupied that we bypass the level of people's deeper concerns. Dr Clyde Narramore says 'every person is worth understanding'.[4]

TAKE CARE WITH HOW YOU SPEAK

When speaking to someone, don't simply give insensitive clichés or quick, easy, 'pat' responses. Paul says in 1 Corinthians 13:1 that eloquence without love is like a 'sounding brass or a clanging cymbal'. Use words that are prompted by love, chosen with care and spoken with tenderness. Proverbs 18:21 says, 'Words kill, words give life; they're either poison or fruit – you choose' (*The Message*). Make every effort today to become a quadraphonic saint and listen with all your heart, in surround sound!

Quote of the day
'When God puts love and compassion in your heart toward others, He's offering you an opportunity to make a difference in their life. You must learn to follow that love. Don't ignore it. Act on it. Somebody needs what you have.'[5] – Joel Osteen

Memory verse for the week

'that there may be no division in the body, but that the _____ may have the same care for one another.' (1 Cor. 12:25, ESV)

Daily Journal

_____

_____

_____

_____

_____

_____

_____

_____

_____

_____

_____

_____

_____

Tips for journeying together: Coming alongside

As well as recognising that you personally send out non-verbal messages and altering them as necessary for the people you are trying to come alongside, remember that they too send out non-verbal cues. Consider what messages other people send out, which may help you understand what they are going through and whether they need your support?

A Community of Grace and Truth

'The Word became flesh and blood, and moved into the neighbourhood. We saw the glory with our own eyes, the one-of-a-kind glory, like Father, like Son, generous inside and out, true from start to finish.' **(John 1:14, *The Message*)**

Jesus has left the Church two gifts to bring to the world, the gospel of truth and the community of grace. In the King James Version, our verse today reads, '[he] dwelt among us, (and we beheld his glory) full of grace and truth' (John 1:14). You could describe this as incarnational love coming alongside us, journeying with us, walking with us, talking with us, making His presence known and felt. Grace here precedes truth, yet in many churches, the emphasis on truth overshadows the outworking of compassionate grace. This is why Jesus gives us the 11th commandment in John 13:34, a new commandment to 'love one another as I have loved you'. He did not say, 'teach one another as I have taught you'. Love by coming alongside is at the very heart of what it is to be human and at the very heart of God. Jim L. Fuller said, 'Live each day as if it were your last, love as if it was your first.'[6]

We are created for community. Eternity and the Godhead are a community. For example, Genesis 1:1 states, 'In the beginning God ...' There you have it, four words into the Bible and you meet God, Elohim, a plural Being! 'Then God said, "Let *us* make mankind in *our* image"' (Gen. 1:26, NIV, author's own emphasis). God, by His very nature, is a trinity of persons, the essence of a loving community. It began in heaven, existing in eternity before time began: God the Father, Son and Holy Spirit living in harmony within the Godhead. 'In the beginning was the Word, and the Word was with God, and the Word was God' (John 1:1).

Satan's purpose in Eden was to disrupt and destroy the community God had created in the Garden and he has been seeking to destroy it ever since. Jesus came from the community of heaven, to restore and establish the community of heaven on earth again, a community whose hallmarks would be grace and truth. The Church is that community, born out of the cross, and care and compassion, coming alongside others, is the incarnational love at its heart.

Grace is an other-centred word; a gracious spirit is gentle, loving, kind, tender-hearted, full of goodness, granting undeserved favour. Grace cares deeply about the needs of others. It compels us to set aside our own needs in order to come alongside and give ourselves extravagantly towards meeting the needs of others. Grace is one-way love. When harnessed to truth, God's glory is revealed in His Church and incarnational love is seen at work. Non-Christians often need a visual aid that reveals the gospel of grace as being good news. Surely in a caring community, where the outworking of grace is the heart of relationships, and truth is the bedrock of our reality, even the hardest heart will melt and the deepest needs will be met? When our communities see our churches overflowing with care and concern, they have seen the miracle of grace and truth at work.

Quote of the day
'Grace is given not to them who speak their faith, but to those who live their faith.'[7] – St Gregory

Memory verse for the week
'that there may be no division in the body, but that the members may have the
_____ _____ for one another.'
(1 Cor. 12:25, ESV)

Daily Journal

_____

_____

_____

_____

_____

_____

_____

_____

_____

_____

_____

_____

_____

_____

_____

Tips for journeying together: Coming alongside
Slow down from your busy activities today. Take time to sit
quietly for 3–5 minutes somewhere outside, on a park bench
or in a garden, looking at God's creative handiwork and
becoming aware of the beauty around you. Then close your
eyes, listening to and identifying the sounds you can hear. Try
to identify at least ten and write them down. This will develop
your sensitivity and help tune your ear to things you may have
not been sensitive to before.

Review

Think back over this week, the sermon content, the daily readings and the memory verse. You could read your Daily Journal entries to refresh your memory of each day. Now jot down one or more comments under the questions below:

- What have I learnt about God this week?

- What have I learnt about others this week?

- What have I learnt about myself this week?

JOURNEYING TOGETHER ACTION PLAN

Again, thinking about what you have learnt this week, write down the names of the two people who you have started to connect with in a meaningful way. If you still do not know their names yet, or if your chosen people have changed, think of a way to ask and then intentionally plan to get alongside them during this next week.

- Church family:

  _____

- Local community/work colleagues:

  _____

Prayer

Father, I am grateful for those who have come alongside and been there for me. Help me to also be a loving, caring person to others on their journey. Amen

Memory verse for the week

'that there may be no division in the body, but that the members may have the same care for one _____.' (1 Cor. 12:25, ESV)

WEEK 3
Journeying

'Stoop down and reach out ...
Share their burdens, and so
complete Christ's law.'
(Gal. 6:1–3, *The Message*)

The Resource of Journey

The Disciples on the Emmaus Road – Luke 24:13–35

Travelling through life

'Your life is a journey you must travel with a deep consciousness of God.' (**1 Pet. 1:18**, *The Message*)

The _____ of the journey

The _____ of the journey

The _____ of the journey

PARAKLESIS – TO CONSOLE

*'our consolation [***paraklesis***] ... abounds through Christ.'*
(**2 Cor. 1:5**)

> **CONSOLATION: Bringing calm and peace, easing and soothing hurt; finding rest and giving hope.**

Connecting with their story

The disiples talk about a living memory and present

_____

Jesus connects and _____

Jesus builds _____

Listening to their story, Jesus:

uses a _____ _____

expresses _____

lets them tell _____ _____

The bigger story

Jesus was carefronting.

> **CAREFRONTING: Shows care and concern for the individual, not just challenging the issue.
> It is not so much trying to change the person but trying to help them see themselves more accurately.**

By carefronting, Jesus:

Earned the right to _____

Helped them face _____

Focused on _____ and hope

To help the disciples see the 'bigger story', Jesus:

- Brings grace and truth (Luke 24:27)

- Ministers to their need (Luke 24:28–30)

- Brings enlightenment (Luke 24:31)

- Re-energises them (Luke 24:33–35)

Sermon Notes

The Journey of Hope

'I will ... turn the "Valley of Trouble" into an "Opportunity of Hope".' **(Hosea 2:15, NET)**

This week we join Jesus as He comes alongside two disconsolate, dispirited, discouraged disciples, who have lost all hope and perspective. They are on the long walk home to Emmaus. Immediately, we see an extremely important principle at work: caring brings hope. It is difficult to care for someone if you are unable to offer them hope. These two wanderers find themselves in a hopeless circumstance, overwhelmed and overcome by their grief and sadness, but the God of all hope in the person of His Son joins them on their journey. And His presence alone brought hope.

There is, of course, natural hope, based on human reasoning and understanding, but the hope these people received that day is the hope that only the presence of Jesus can bring. This word 'hope' in Scripture is not a statement of wishful thinking, a longed-for pipedream or a flight of fancy; it is not 'Oh I do hope things will get better for you'. In Scripture, hope is not simply the desire for something good in the future, hope is the reason that enables us to find strength for what we long for in the future. Alex Elle said, 'I am thankful for my struggle because without it, I wouldn't have stumbled upon my strength.'[1]

We have hope for living because Jesus is the reason for living, and our trust is in Him. Hope is a term of assurance, certainty and conviction; that's why Paul says, 'We have this hope as an anchor for the soul' (Heb. 6:19, NIV). Christian hope does not encourage people to deny the reality of their circumstances, on the contrary, it faces reality with the assurance and conviction that God's grace is sufficient for every circumstance of life. It is a hope that rests on the fact that God is all-wise, all-knowing and all-compassionate. However, such a truth is not easy to grasp when people are struggling under pressure. Hope comes in the shape of people who will come alongside, walk beside us and journey with us through our valley of trouble. We are 'working together and ...

struggling side by side to get others to believe the good news' (Phil. 1:27, CEV). Life is a struggle but we can learn to 'struggle well' together.

God calls us to be a door of hope. Has He not promised that when we ask, we will receive; when we knock, it will be opened; when we seek, we will find? So like Jesus with these disheartened, hurting people on the road to Emmaus, we must be swift to come to the side of those who are burdened, to lighten their load in times of trouble. It is our willingness to journey with them that becomes a door of hope. Take time to open up that door to someone today.

Quote of the day

'Hope has two beautiful daughters; their names are Anger and Courage; anger at the way things are, and courage to see that they do not remain the way they are.'[2] – St Augustine

Memory verse for the week

'Praise be to the God and Father of our Lord Jesus Christ, the Father of _____ and the God of all comfort, who comforts us in all our troubles, so that we can comfort those in any trouble with the comfort we ourselves receive from God.' (2 Cor. 1:3–4, NIV)

Daily Journal

_____

_____

_____

_____

_____

_____

_____

_____

_____

_____

_____

_____

_____

_____

_____

_____

Tips for journeying together: Be a good listener
Most of us are better talkers than listeners. But as we have two ears and one mouth let's try to listen twice as much as we speak. Why not make the effort today to talk less and listen more?

An Enlightened Journey

'I pray that the eyes of your heart may be enlightened'
(Eph. 1:18, NASB)

A loss of hope is usually linked to a loss of perspective. Paul, incarcerated, stripped of ministry, a prisoner of Rome, writes to the church at Ephesus, which was not made up of professionally religious people but ordinary working people who were being persecuted and martyred. Despite his own difficult circumstances he gives thanks to God 'who has blessed us with all spiritual blessings in heavenly places in Christ ... chosen us ... made us accepted in the beloved ... adoption as children ... we have redemption ... the forgiveness of sin ... made known to us the mystery of His will ... in whom also we obtained an inheritance ... sealed with the Holy Spirit of promise' (vv3–14). In the midst of privation and hardship, these were Paul's realities. In the words of St Francis of Assisi, 'O Divine Master, grant that I may not so much seek to be consoled as to console; to be understood as to understand; to be loved as to love.'[3] Despite his personal struggles, Paul prays in the light of his own hope for the Ephesians, that in the midst of their trying circumstances, the eyes of their hearts would also be opened.

The Greek verb here is *photizo*, meaning 'to illuminate or let light into darkness', like a camera shutter that opens, capturing the beauty of the reality that is before it. It is the word from which we get our English word 'photograph'. There are times on our journey when light dims, perspective darkens, focus becomes blurred and hope fades. We find ourselves hemmed in by a spiritual fog as struggles and troubles crowd in upon us. It is in these moments when the valley of trouble (from yesterday's reading) seems to be such a dark place that we need fellow travellers to come alongside and journey with us, bringing a shaft of light.

Paul prays that light and perspective will flood the hearts of the followers of Jesus, in three areas:

1. PURPOSE FOR THE JOURNEY

'That you may know ... the hope to which he has called you' (v18, NIV). Here Paul writes of the assurance, certainty and conviction of God's calling, purpose and plan for the past, present, and future. There is a certain future unfolding for you on your journey – not an 'I hope so', but an 'I know so!'

2. RESOURCES FOR THE JOURNEY

'That you may know ... what are the riches of his glorious inheritance in the saints' (v18, ESV). Our great resource for our journey is Christ's grace and truth. And Paul doesn't say riches for the saints, but in the saints, realising and embracing the rightful inheritance God has deposited in us.

3. STRENGTH AND ENERGY FOR THE JOURNEY

'That you may know ... his incomparably great power for us who believe. That power is the same as the mighty strength he exerted when he raised Christ from the dead' (vv19–20, NIV). Paul encourages us to draw from the resurrection life and power of God. His story, within our story, transforms our lives, helping us recover from divorce, redundancy, drugs, crime, business failure, family breakdown and depression. What is more, through His power in our story – strength and grace can also be imparted to others.

Quote of the day

'It's funny how, in this journey of life, even though we may begin at different times and places, our paths cross with others so that we may share our love, compassion, observations, and hope. This is a design of God that I appreciate and cherish.' [4] – Steve Maraboli

Memory verse for the week

'Praise be to the God and Father of our Lord Jesus Christ, the Father of compassion and the _____ _____ _____ _____, who comforts us in all our troubles, so that we can comfort those in any trouble with the comfort we ourselves receive from God.' (2 Cor. 1:3–4, NIV)

Daily Journal

_____

_____

_____

_____

_____

_____

_____

_____

_____

_____

Tips for journeying together: Be a good listener
Learn to listen to what is *not* being said. For example, if someone only talks about one parent, you could sensitively ask them how their relationship is or was with their other parent. This may open up the opportunity for them to share on a deeper level.

Fellow Travellers

'It's better to have a partner than go it alone. Share the work, share the wealth. And if one falls down, the other helps, but if there's no one to help, tough!' (**Eccl. 4:9–10, *The Message***)

We have seen that the first step to journeying is the willingness to walk with someone in their valley of trouble. Our reassuring presence brings hope and consolation. As the Beatles tell us, in their 1967 album *Sgt. Pepper's Lonely Hearts Club Band*, we can get by with a little help from our friends. Joining someone on their journey says 'I care', but Jesus did more. He is in this journey for the long haul, He cares enough to commit to the journey. Caring is a commitment, an action of the will that embraces the truth that 'It is more blessed to give than to receive' (Acts 20:35).

To be a fellow traveller with someone on the journey of life is a commitment of time and resources. The idea of such a commitment can strike fear into our hearts. We can worry we will not have what it takes, and like the disciples at the feeding of the 5,000, we may feel inadequate for the task. 'I am not a counsellor, psychotherapist, experienced social worker or pastor,' we say, 'that hurting person needs expert help I cannot give.'

When I was diagnosed with kidney cancer, my world was thrown into confusion. Although my family and I knew the same God was with us and that He had not changed, our circumstances had. They brought with them a new set of unfamiliar challenges as I faced major surgery to remove the malignant tumour and diseased kidney. Unwittingly, we had entered into a valley of trouble. In these difficult days of adjustment, we did not need a professional counsellor, psychotherapist or a cognitive behavioural therapist to help us in our struggle, but fellow travellers who had been this way before, who could journey with us in our hour of need. I called someone I knew who had trod that pathway before us, who became a fellow traveller and companion on our recovery journey, and like Jesus with the Emmaus Road disciples, they brought hope, commitment and consolation to our lives.

But they also brought something else. I describe this as their 'resource of journey' – their personal life experience and journey with cancer, grace and truth. Through this person, we received strength, encouragement, healing and insight as we were sustained through a difficult passage in our journey. How sad that in the Church, this huge resource (people's experience on their own journeys) is seemingly often neglected, wasted or untapped. These journey experiences should be spiritual resources, made available to us through Jesus Christ in the family of God. Such a wealth of life experience deposited in the lives of God's people – people, who in their lives have experienced deep issues of the soul and life circumstances. Paul writes, 'I feel certain that you, my brothers, have real Christian character and experience, and that you are capable of keeping each other on the right road' (Rom. 15:14, Phillips). Are you one of these people? Then make a commitment today to let God use your resource of journey to come alongside others.

Quote of the day

'Many Christians estimate difficulty in the light of their own resources, and thus they attempt very little and they always fail. All giants have been weak men who did great things for God because they reckoned on His power and presence to be with them.'[5] – Hudson Taylor

Memory verse for the week

'Praise be to the God and Father of our Lord Jesus Christ, the Father of compassion and the God of all comfort, _____ _____

_____ in all our troubles, so that we can comfort those in any trouble with the comfort we ourselves receive from God.' (2 Cor. 1:3–4, NIV)

Daily Journal

_____

_____

_____

_____

_____

_____

_____

_____

_____

_____

_____

_____

_____

_____

_____

Tips for journeying together: Be a good listener

Listen to gain information, not thinking what you are going to say next and preparing to say it as soon as the other person finishes talking. Their responses are not punctuation for your sentences. Remember, good listening isn't about giving advice, or solutions – that is talking!

The Listening Journey

'It is best to listen much' **(James 1:19, TLB)**

Consolation and hope take root when we begin to feel someone is taking time to listen to our story, and then to walk and talk with us as Jesus did with the Emmaus Road disciples. So often we think that to help, we have got to do something. We feel an unspoken pressure to make something positive happen. But we don't always need to 'do' something; sometimes we just need to 'be' something. After all, Jesus taught the *beatitudes*, not 'do' attitudes. Simply listening is a strong sign of consolation and gives a hurting person hope, and that is the start of the journey. C.H. Spurgeon said, 'Consolation is the dropping of a gentle dew from heaven on desert hearts beneath. True consolation, such as can reach the heart, must be one of the choicest gifts of divine mercy.'[6]

I remember, some years ago, going to visit a friend whose wife had died, leaving him with their two young teenage children. Amidst tears, he unburdened his heart and deep grief for some minutes then went silent. I sat with him in the silence for about 25 minutes and then said, 'John, I think it is time for me to go now.' At the door, he said, 'Trevor, I have received many well-meaning cards and calls from friends and family, but I haven't yet been able to take their sentiments in. Unburdening my heart to you, and you sitting in the silence with me, saying nothing but being a reassuring presence, has meant more to me at this time than all the well-meaning messages I have received. People have meant well with what they have said, but it just hasn't registered yet.' I journeyed with John and the children over the next months as they processed their grief and loss.

One of the most caring things we can do for people is to listen to them. J.B. Phillips' translation of our verse today puts it like this: 'Dear brothers, let every man be quick to listen but slow to use his tongue.' Listening is one of the great tangible expressions of loving. So often, when trying to resolve marital issues, I have heard from a husband or wife 'but they just don't listen to me', the inference being, 'if they truly loved me, they would listen to me'. Proverbs 18:2 (NIV) reads, 'Fools find no pleasure in understanding but delight in airing their own opinions.'

Listening means concentrating on a person's story so intently you become more aware of the other person than you are of yourself. As you listen, ask yourself questions like this: 'How would I feel if this was my story? How would I react if this had happened to me?' Then using your expressions, eye contact and understanding nods, you can convey that they have your full attention, concern and awareness. Listening enables people to tell the story of their journey thus far, in their own way and in their own time.

Quote of the day
'No journey is complete that does not lead through some dark valleys. We can properly comfort others only with the comfort wherewith we ourselves have been comforted by God.'[7]
– Vance Havner

Memory verse for the week

'Praise be to the God and Father of our Lord Jesus Christ, the Father of compassion and the God of all comfort, who comforts us _____ _____

_____ _____ so that we can comfort those in any trouble with the comfort we ourselves receive from God.' (2 Cor. 1:3–4, NIV)

Daily Journal

_____

_____

_____

_____

_____

_____

_____

_____

_____

_____

_____

_____

_____

Tips for journeying together: Be a good listener
Good listening really focuses on what the other person is saying. Try to be genuine, not twiddling your thumbs, looking regularly at your watch or out of the window.

The Journey of Understanding

'be eager to show respect for one another' **(Rom. 12:10, GNB)**

To journey well with others, we need the ability to treat those with whom we are journeying with the profoundest respect. When Jesus came alongside these disciples, He did not belittle them or approach them in a superior attitude, judging them, categorising them, labelling or manipulating them, but came alongside them with the attitude, 'I know you are struggling; help me understand your predicament.' He knew how to differentiate between the presenting problem and their deep struggle. As we have seen, this was one of the secrets of our Lord's success in His caring relationship with people: He spent time showing love, concern and a willingness to bear their burdens. Is it any wonder that He was known as 'the friend of sinners'? When He met the woman at the well, He did not condemn her, He showed respect and engaged her in a conversation about her need for water. It wasn't long before He was talking about her deeper thirst, and the deep relational struggles and moral failure of her life.

Understanding is not just recognition of the presenting problem, or even the root cause, but understanding the underlying need. Effective Christian caring always ministers to the underlying needs, not simply the surface issues that are so often presented. People often need to feel understood before they will take on board what people trying to help have to say, but how do we get across to someone struggling on their journey that we understand them and the issues of their story? Well, we need to journey with people at their pace, don't hurry them, let them talk it out and unburden their heart. We must 'share each other's troubles and problems' (Gal. 6:2, TLB).

Having listened well, we can show understanding by reflecting back to the person, in a paraphrased form, a summary of their story, as we are coming to understand it. (I stress the word 'paraphrased' because there is nothing more disconcerting than retelling a person's story back to them verbatim, parrot fashion!) How does this help? It shows the person that you have grasped and comprehended their story, and gives them the reassurance that, even though you might not have a solution to the immediate issues they face, at least you understand and care. Being understood is often as helpful to someone's emotions as good advice is to satisfying the mind.

Sometimes it is possible to be so over-sympathetic and overwhelmed by people's struggles that we become too subjective. My observation is that an overly sympathetic nature usually results from our own inner hurts that have never been healed. These are then highlighted whenever we come in contact with someone who is also hurting. If this is our situation, then we can ask God to heal us of our inner hurts.

Quote of the day
'Be assured, if you walk with Him and look to Him, and expect help from Him, He will never fail you.'[8] – George Muller

Memory verse for the week

'Praise be to the God and Father of our Lord Jesus Christ, the Father of compassion and the God of all comfort, who comforts us in all our troubles, so that we can _____

_____ _____ _____

_____ with the comfort we ourselves receive from God.' (2 Cor. 1:3–4, NIV)

Daily Journal

_____

_____

_____

_____

_____

_____

_____

_____

_____

_____

_____

_____

_____

_____

_____

_____

_____

_____

Tips for journeying together: Be a good listener
Respect other people's opinions. Even if you do not share
them or agree with them, hear the other person out
respectfully. Do not assume that the way you see things is
the only way. Good listeners show consideration for other
people's views and ideas.

Review

Think back over this week, the sermon content, the daily readings and the memory verse. You could read your Daily Journal entries to refresh your memory of each day. Now jot down one or more comments under the questions below:

· What more have I learnt about God this week?

· What have I learnt about others this week?

· What have I learnt about myself this week?

JOURNEYING TOGETHER ACTION PLAN

This week, think about beginning to journey alongside those you have connected with in the last few weeks. Write down their names again here and consider meaningful ways through which you could start to journey with them.

- Church family:

  _____

- Local community/work colleagues:

  _____

Prayer
Lord, time is too short and life is too serious for me not to journey with others. Help me to make expressing Your life in me a priority. Amen.

Memory verse for the week

'Praise be to the God and Father of our Lord Jesus Christ, the Father of compassion and the God of all comfort, who comforts us in all our troubles, so that we can comfort those in any trouble with

_____ _____ _____

_____ _____

from God.' (2 Cor. 1:3–4, NIV)

The gift of your journey
Now you have come to the end of Week 3, this would be a good time (if you haven't already) for you to turn to the back of this book and complete the gift of your journey exercise.

Living

'Gently encourage the
stragglers, and reach out for
the exhausted, pulling them to
their feet. Be patient with each
person, attentive to individual
needs ... Look for the best in
each other, and always do your
best to bring it out.'
(1 Thess. 5:13–15, *The Message*)

Choose Life

The Man by the Pool of Bethesda – John 5:1–15

Direction for the journey

> 'Your life is a journey you must travel with a deep consciousness of God.' **(1 Pet. 1:18, *The Message*)**

PARAKALEO: **TO EXHORT**

> 'like a father with his children, we exhorted [**parakaleo**] each one of you and encouraged you and charged you to lead a life worthy of God' **(1 Thess. 2:11–12, RSV)**

> **EXHORTATION: Bringing clear spiritual direction, guidance and understanding: focused on developing wise life choices that shape behaviour patterns and life outcomes.**

Exhortation is spiritual _____

Life in a new dimension

Bios = _____ life (Luke 8:14)

Psuche = _____ life (Luke 9:24)

Zoe = _____ life (John 1:1–4; 10:10; 14:6)

'Now a certain man was there who had an infirmity thirty-eight years.' **(John 5:5)**

His outer world (*bios*) was:

A _____ and unpleasant place

An uncertain and _____ place

A picture of life today?

The burden of _____

The challenge of _____

In His inner world (*psuche*), he had:

Self-_____

Given up and become _____

Settled for a _____ mentality

The directive to change

'Jesus said to him, "Get up! Pick up your mat and walk."'
(John 5:8, NIV)

We don't always choose what _____ in life

We have the _____ to choose what we do with it

Life is a _____ of choices

We are _____ for our choices

Choices are always _____

The loss of felt choice is not the loss of _____
choice

We can choose to live _____ kind of life

'Where is the man who fears the Lord? God will teach him how to choose the best.' **(Psa. 25:12, TLB)**

Pitiful or Powerful?

Sermon Notes

Meeting Discouragement

'We use our powerful God-tools for smashing warped philosophies, tearing down barriers erected against the truth of God, fitting every loose thought and emotion and impulse into the structure of life shaped by Christ.'
(2 Cor. 10:5, *The Message*)

This week, we turn our attention to look at some common life struggles that emerge as we journey alongside those who need our help. It is important that we take the time to understand some of the difficulties and issues people wrestle with in their hearts and minds. By discovering a little more about these issues, it will enable us to develop our ability to help. The Gospel account we are considering this week is the man by the pool of Bethesda. For 38 years, he lay waiting for the waters to move, and every time they did, someone else beat him to it and got in first. What a dispiriting and discouraging way to spend each day, going from hope to despair.

Discouragement is an issue many people grapple with. Sometimes, life just doesn't seem fair and this can drag us down to the depths of depression. You will hear discouraged people say, 'Things are hopeless', 'They will never change', 'What's the use of trying?' and 'I give up'. In a world such as this, we are easily discouraged and dispirited. How can we come alongside others overtaken by discouragement? Here again, we meet it sensitively, lovingly and with compassion – listening, understanding and showing our concern.

Have you ever noticed how our emotions are affected by our thinking? At times, it can be possible to stop feeling discouraged by an act of will, but this can be difficult. However, if someone helps us to re-align our thinking like Jesus did with the Emmaus Road disciples, then feelings of discouragement can respond accordingly. Learn to tune into what a person is thinking, then very gently ask these questions: 'Is that really the case?', 'Is there proof of that?', 'Could there be some other explanation?'. Ask yourself whether they are interpreting the discouraging situation correctly? Often, more than anything else, discouraged people need to find hope and gain a fresh perspective on life. This can often come from a caring friend who can gently challenge and help change the discouraged person's thinking and conclusions.

In this week's Bible reading, the man by the pool clearly had physical issues that were the source of his discouragement. Research carried out on the subject of discouragement supports that occasionally discouragement can be linked to physical factors. Therefore, if a person is discouraged for a considerable period of time, it could be due to these sorts of issues: poor sleeping habits, a stressful lifestyle, a chemical imbalance, physical infection, improper diet or over commitment at work. Obviously, prayer is a good place to start when dealing with physical ailments, but, if after prayer there is no perceptible change, it may be a good idea to encourage a medical check-up. If no physical causes are found, help can be given by showing a person how to change their thinking and life patterns, as our verse for today says, 'fitting every loose thought and emotion and impulse into the structure of life shaped by Christ'.

Quote of the day

'When you are tempted to get discouraged, remind yourself that, according to God's Word, your future is getting brighter; you are on your way to a new level of glory. You may think you've got a long way to go, but you need to look back at how far you've already come.'[1] – Joel Osteen

Memory verse for the week

'_____ one another's burdens, and so fulfil the law of Christ.' (Gal. 6:2, ESV)

Daily Journal

_____

_____

_____

_____

_____

_____

_____

_____

_____

_____

_____

_____

_____

_____

_____

_____

Tips for journeying together: Be an empathiser
Take the time to understand someone's attitude and circumstances without judging them for it. You never really understand a person until you first consider things from their point of view.

Terrible Twins

'So the other disciples told him, "We have seen the Lord!" But he said to them, 'Unless I see the nail marks in his hands and put my finger where the nails were, and put my hand into his side, I will not believe.' **(John 20:25, NIV)**

Discouragement and doubt are linked together. They are terrible twins. When Jesus spoke with the deeply discouraged man by the pool of Bethesda, his response was that he doubted it would ever change. He was effectively saying, 'But Lord, you don't understand, it's always been this way.' Last week, we also saw that a major issue for the Emmaus Road disciples was the doubt they expressed. They effectively said, 'we had hoped, but ... ' 'But' is a word of doubt, and whenever you hear it expressed, you know doubts exist as hope fades. Faced with difficult, discouraging circumstances, negative thinking kicks in, and doubts arise.

The Emmaus Road disciples doubted that Jesus had even been the Christ, the Messiah. Recently, an English paper reported that the 'Archbishop of Canterbury admits sometimes he has moments of doubt'.[2] The article goes on to say that, from time to time, the Right Honourable, The Most Reverend Justin Welby confesses to having doubts on issues of his faith. Doubt is part of our human frailty and weakness. In today's Bible passage, Thomas, another close follower of Christ, expressed his own doubt and need for evidence.

You will discover that doubt is another common struggle that people succumb to from time to time. People will express self-doubt about themselves, their judgments, their adequacy; about others, their loyalty, their truthfulness, their reliability; and on matters of faith, such as God's love for them, whether He answers prayer, or whether the Bible is true.

How do we care for those who doubt? We must not allow ourselves to be critical or dismissive when coming alongside those struggling in difficult circumstances who express their despair and doubt. Don't be in too much of a hurry to give answers. What a person often needs is the reassurance of your presence and the stability that your faith and confidence in God brings. Get alongside the doubting person and show, through listening and understanding, that you care. Isn't this what Jesus did with those Emmaus Road disciples? He saw their doubt and could have dismissed it with the words: 'I am the Lord.' However, He waited, listened, showed care, then when He knew they were ready for insight, He care-fronted their doubt by consoling them and sharing another perspective.

What we should not do is say such things as, 'Stop doubting' or 'Pull yourself together'. That rarely helps. It is far more helpful to listen with compassion, acceptance and love, even though, in listening, you may hear things that are concerning. Keep in mind, as you listen, that most people's doubts are not in the mind but in the heart. Some doubts are intellectual but most are emotional. By that, I mean the person may be carrying some deep emotional pain that causes them to question the truth and reality of their circumstances or their intellectual beliefs.

Quote of the day

'Christ never failed to distinguish between doubt and unbelief. Doubt is "can't believe". Unbelief is "won't believe". Doubt is honesty. Unbelief is obstinacy. Doubt is looking for light. Unbelief is content with darkness.'[3] – Henry Drummond

Memory verse for the week

'Bear _____ _____ burdens, and so fulfil the law of Christ.' (Gal. 6:2, ESV)

Daily Journal

_____

_____

_____

_____

_____

_____

_____

_____

_____

_____

_____

_____

_____

_____

_____

_____

Tips for journeying together: Be an empathiser
Try not to say 'I know just how you feel' too much as, although
well-meaning, it can sometimes sound insincere. It is better
to say, 'I can tell you are struggling with ... and that must be
difficult for you.'

Stress Busters

'Are you tired? Worn out? Burned out on religion? Come to me. Get away with me and you'll recover your life. I'll show you how to take a real rest. Walk with me and work with me – watch how I do it. Learn the unforced rhythms of grace. I won't lay anything heavy or ill-fitting on you. Keep company with me and you'll learn to live freely and lightly.'
(Matt. 11:28–30, *The Message*)

Another common life issue is stress. The World Health Organisation has described stress as the epidemic of the twenty-first century [4] and it was recently reported that the third most popular gifts are stress balls, also known as stress relievers or stress busters. [5] I heard about a man who woke up stressed one Sunday morning and said to his wife, 'It's no good, I am stressed out, and there are three reasons why I am not going to church today: I don't like the people, I don't like the pastor, and I am the pastor.' Stress affects us all, and we can all have days like that.

Stress is defined as the conflict between demands placed on us, and an inner feeling of inability or inadequacy to meet them. Stress is accompanied by anxiety, the troublesome feeling that makes us uneasy and apprehensive when concerned with real or imagined challenges. They do not always appear to spring from any rational cause, and sometimes we can be anxious without knowing what exactly we are anxious about. Stress, on the other hand, has traceable causes. We usually stress about things that can be identified. This is where someone coming alongside can more objectively help us identify 'stressors'. However, the source of our stress isn't usually the difficulties, circumstances and situations themselves. Instead, it is often our attitude and approach towards them. Jesus said in John 14:27 (AMPC), 'Stop allowing yourselves to be agitated and disturbed'.

Our verse today paints a picture not of striving but of flowing, not of stressing but of resting, not of worrying but of trusting. As the former slave trader John Newton wrote in his 1779 hymn, *Amazing Grace*, grace changes everything. Grace does not free us from struggle, it enables us to 'struggle well'. Grace does not restrict us, it releases us. It is not something to be earned but a gift to be received. Grace may not change the circumstance but it will change us, our attitude and our approach.

Writing to the Philippians, Paul says, 'Don't worry about anything; instead, pray about everything; tell God your needs' (Phil. 4:6, TLB). Rest comes from an attitude of trust, and trust comes from putting ourselves and our affairs in God's hands. This is a good model to follow when coming alongside those who are stressed and anxious. To stop stressing is not simply to put it out of our minds – that will only last for a short while, and then anxiousness will return. God's way is to *replace* the stress and worry. The secret is simple: tell God about everything, then trust Him for 'the unforced rhythms of grace', and 'learn to live freely and lightly'.

Quote of the day
'Don't stress over anything today that God is not stressed over.'[6]
– Louie Giglio

Memory verse for the week

'Bear one another's burdens, and so _____ the law of Christ' (Gal. 6:2, ESV)

Daily Journal

_____

_____

_____

_____

_____

_____

_____

_____

_____

_____

_____

_____

_____

_____

_____

_____

_____

Tips for journeying together: Be an empathiser
When you engage in conversation today, be alert to the
subtle signals people often send out when they are stressed.
Uncharacteristic reactions, indecisiveness, sighing, anxious
looks, speaking too loudly or too quietly, a furrowed brow –
any of these may be an indication of stress.

Time is of the Essence

'Live life, then, with a due sense of responsibility, not as men who do not know the meaning and purpose of life but as those who do. Make the best use of your time, despite all the difficulties of these days. Don't be vague but firmly grasp what you know to be the will of God.' **(Eph. 5:15–17, Phillips)**

Yesterday, we were considering stress. Have you ever wished for a thirty-six hour day? Surely it would relieve pressure and stress, and resolve the issue of feeling like there is not enough time to get everything done? Often our lives are full of frenetic activity, leaving a trail of unfinished tasks. In our verses today, Paul addresses the issue of time as a sacred trust, given by God to use and invest conscientiously and wisely. The demands of modern life give rise to what someone has called 'the tyranny of the urgent', a term used to describe the habit of always doing what is most pressing, instead of taking the time to work out a proper order of priorities.

Numerous books and courses have been written on time management, but actually time is impossible to manage. It is constant: sixty seconds a minute, sixty minutes an hour, twenty-four hours a day, seven days a week. Paul doesn't say manage your time but 'make best use of it'. The issue is not time management, but management of *ourselves*. You see, we can't manage time, but we can learn to manage ourselves. Some years ago, a lady wrote to me. At the time, I was part of a rapidly growing and developing Christian ministry and I had taken on more responsibility than I ought to have done. She said the Lord woke her up in the night and told her that I was in deep bondage, bound by chains of schedules and imprisoned in dungeons of administration. She said she was praying for me, as Satan was robbing me of my God-given calling through a continuous treadmill of activity. She encouraged me to make changes and choices. How grateful I have been for those timely words of exhortation.

How do we care for people caught in the 'busy-busy syndrome', or stricken with 'hurry-hurry sickness'? Well, I hope by now it is quite clear that all struggles should be met by good listening, understanding, compassion and prayer. Having said that, let's get to the heart of the issue. God has given us time to be a servant; unfortunately, time has made us its slave, pushing us around from one thing to the next. As today's Bible reading says, 'Don't be vague' – be decisive and take responsibility. Make some choices. We need to put first things first, omit lesser things and determine God's priorities in our lives. Start by taking stock and evaluating just where time is being spent. Unless we stop and sort out the multiplicity of tasks, we will always run ourselves ragged, doing a lot but accomplishing little. When we stop to evaluate, it's clear the problem is not a shortage of time but the use of our time. 'Firmly grasp what you know to be the will of the Lord.' Recognise the excessive demands, take control of your world, choose life and re-order your world in the light of eternal values, 'living life with a due sense of responsibility'.

Quote of the day
'Though I am always in haste, I am never in a hurry, because I never undertake more work than I can go through with calmness of spirit.'[7] – John Wesley

Memory verse for the week
'Bear one another's burdens, and so fulfil the

_____ of Christ.' (Gal. 6:2, ESV)

Daily Journal

_____

_____

_____

_____

_____

_____

_____

_____

_____

_____

_____

_____

_____

_____

_____

_____

_____

Tips for journeying together: Be an empathiser
Empathy gives a person space to think and feel, and often a few moments of silence is important to them. Don't hurry a silence or badger a person with questions when they pause. Let them tell their story in their own words and in their own time.

Putting the Pieces Together

'You're blessed when you feel you've lost what is most dear to you. Only then can you be embraced by the One most dear to you.' **(Matt. 5:4, *The Message*)**

A startling thing about the sayings of Jesus is that at first they seem so counter-intuitive. He said that to live we have to die, to receive we have to give, to save life we must lose it, if struck on one cheek we should offer the other, and, in our verse today, 'blessed are those who mourn' (KJV). Mourning has to do with loss, and loss in one form or another touches all of us. Everybody will need to deal with this at some point in their lives. Shattered dreams, broken promises, disappointment, relationships, friendships, redundancy, divorce, business failure, personal failure, financial loss and bereavement. Loss is a recurring theme in all of these life circumstances.

The man by the pool of Bethesda had clearly lost hope. Loss of hope was also in the heart of both the Emmaus Road disciples. Loss at any level is painful, and pain comes in all shapes and sizes. It brings with it a deep sense of grief that impacts our emotions – painful feelings of emptiness, isolation, loneliness and a sense of confusion and bewilderment that can quickly turn to blame, anger, bitterness and resentment.

I have often heard people talk about 'recovering' from a loss, but I'm not convinced of that language. Personally, I'm not sure people ever fully recover from a major loss. What is gone is gone. The reality of life is that some things can just never quite be the same again, some circumstances cannot be recreated, those we love deeply can never be replaced. We may not recover what we have lost, but we can be restored by God and released from its pain to face life again. This is the message of the cross. Whatever may have been robbed from our lives, God restores us in Jesus, enabling us to live life again.

So, how can we help people to face their loss? Well, we can be part of the blessing in their mourning that Jesus talks about here. The first thing to recognise is that loss means learning to deal and cope with change and adjustment. Restoration means a period of readjustment. Gently help them to admit their feelings of loss. Issues can never be effectively processed until we admit they exist. Share with them that it is not a weakness to lean on others at such a time. Assure them that your time and presence is not given grudgingly but willingly and freely. Encourage them not to make any major decisions at present. Some people rebound at times of loss, seeking to compensate by rushing prematurely into new commitments. Make yourself available (daily, if possible) so they can talk with you and pray with you, sharing their thoughts and feelings. Experiencing loss is better handled when there is someone around like you, who, although you may not have many answers, is willing to journey alongside with a consoling, comforting presence.

Quote of the day

'In times of loss, choose your faith instead of lose your faith. The fact is, a major loss can either lift you or lower you, it can either deepen your faith, or cheapen your faith.'[8] – Bradley Kellam

Memory verse for the week

'Bear one another's burdens, and so fulfil the law of _____.' (Gal. 6:2, ESV)

Daily Journal

_____

_____

_____

_____

_____

_____

_____

_____

_____

_____

_____

_____

_____

_____

_____

_____

_____

_____

WEEK 4
LIVING

Tips for journeying together: Be an empathiser
Sometimes tears express a needed emotional release but
occasionally they can be distracting. Empathetic listening
knows when to be moved to tears and when to remain deeply
interested but emotionally objective, not being overwhelmed
by the other person's emotion.

Review

Think back over this week, the sermon content, the daily readings and the memory verse. You could read your Daily Journal entries to refresh your memory of each day. Now jot down one or more comments under the questions below:

- What more have I learnt about God this week?

- What have I learnt about others this week?

- What have I learnt about myself this week?

JOURNEYING TOGETHER ACTION PLAN

Think about how you have started to journey with the people you have decided to connect with. Consider here how you have started to journey with them already and what you think your next steps could be to further your journey together.

- Church family:

  _____

- Local community/work colleagues:

  _____

Prayer

Lord, the more I realise how many people who intersect with my life are struggling, the more I feel compelled to come alongside. Deepen my compassion and concern for them as the days go by that I might truly be that person that You can use in their lives. Amen.

Memory verse for the week

'Bear one another's burdens, and so fulfil the law of Christ.' (_____, ESV)

Healing

'That's exactly what Jesus did. He didn't make it easy for himself by avoiding people's troubles, but waded right in and helped out. "I took on the troubles of the troubled," is the way Scripture puts it.' (Rom. 15:3–4, *The Message*)

Strong at the Broken Places

The Woman in the Temple – Luke 13:10–17

Strength for the journey

> *'Now we who are strong ought to bear the weaknesses of the weak, and not to please ourselves. Let each one of us please his neighbor for that which is good, to be building him up.'*
> **(Rom. 15:1–2, WEB)**

PARAKALEO – TO COMFORT

> *'So comfort [***parakaleo***] each other and make each other strong'* **(1 Thess. 5:11, NLV, author's own emphasis)**

> **COMFORT: Coming alongside someone at a broken place and journeying with them to strengthen and build them up, helping them find healing, wholeness and inner fortitude.**

> *'Bear one another's burdens, and so fulfil the law of Christ.'*
> **(Gal. 6:2)**

> *'we must always aim at those things that bring peace and that help strengthen one another.'* **(Rom. 14:19, GNB)**

The woman had:

A pitiful _____

A physical _____

An _____ spirit

The human struggle

'Human life is a struggle, isn't it? It's a life sentence to hard labor.' (**Job 7:1, *The Message***)

_____ infirmities

_____ assessments

'They have also healed the hurt of My people slightly, Saying, "Peace, peace!" When there is no peace.' (**Jer. 6:14**)

Seeing Beneath the Waterline

1. Recognise all _____ is caused

2. Acknowledge the _____ places

   Relationships

   Dreams

   Heart

   Image

   Cisterns

   Body

3. Explore the pool of

   _____

4. Identify a _____ spirit

Forgiveness

GRACE FROM GOD

5. Becoming _____

   at the broken places

Respond to God's grace

> 'Be careful that none of you fails to respond to the grace which God gives, for if he does there can very easily spring up in him a bitter spirit which is not only bad in itself but can also poison the lives of many others.' **(Heb. 12:15, Phillips)**

Choose the pathway of forgiveness

> 'bearing with one another, and forgiving one another, if anyone has a complaint against another; even as Christ forgave you, so you also must do.' **(Col. 3:13)**

Be loosed and lifted

We don't have to be bound by the crippling wounds of the past, or live with the pain of the present. We don't have to live at a broken place, we can be liberated and set free in Jesus' name.

Sermon Notes

Don't Shoot the Wounded!

'We who are strong have an obligation to bear with the failings of the weak, and not to please ourselves. Let each of us please his neighbor for his good, to build him up.'
(Rom. 15:1–2, ESV)

Now we are in week five, let's continue exploring how we can journey alongside others. Jesus described the Holy Spirit as the 'Comforter' whom He would send to empower, energise and strengthen our lives. Oh, how we underestimate this powerful spiritual balm of comfort for the wounded soul! We are most like the Holy Spirit when we come alongside others with His comforting strength. Strength is needed because of the inherent weakness and struggle of our own humanness. God's plan is to take our weaknesses and turn them into strengths so, like the apostle Paul, we can say that His strength is made perfect in our weakness (2 Cor. 12:9).

At times we all feel weak, that's because we are. In fact, God doesn't often choose strong people, but weak ones in whom He can reveal His strength. One translation puts it as, 'my power shows up best in weak people' (2 Cor. 12:9, TLB). Does that mean we should stay weak and wallow in self-pity? No! It is clear from Scripture that Paul could have been such a candidate. He was troubled by a thorn in the flesh, and we know that thorns wound, hurt and bring pain. However he said that because of God's strength, 'I rather glory in my infirmities' (2 Cor. 12:9, KJV).

Week upon week, we are seeing that things that happen in life wound and weaken us. Unfortunately, some people never seem to recover from the bruising blows that strike them. Their hearts seemingly still reel and bleed from the deep wounds of hurt, horror and hatred. These people can travel through life as walking wounded, who like war veterans live with the war continuing to rage inside them, even though the battle ended a long time ago.

Chuck Girard, an American gospel singer, wrote, 'don't shoot the wounded, someday you might be one'.[1] Similarly, Annie Dillard said that 'maybe we

WEEK 5 HEALING

105

ought to hand people safety helmets rather than hymnals when they arrive for worship!'[2] It has also been said that, 'The church are the only group of people who don't look after their wounded.' How sad to think this may be the case! This is why we need to come alongside each other, to pour comfort, strength and healing into the wounded and weak. This is what today's reading says: 'Now we who are strong have an obligation to bear the weaknesses of those without strength.'

The thing is, in God's economy, wounds can be healed and weakness turned to strength. When God heals a wound, it no longer remains a bleeding, open sore. Have you been so wounded by life that you feel an overwhelming sense of weakness? Then take heart – God's strength is available, and He might just use others to bring it to you. You can become strong again at the broken places if you will allow the divine 'Comforter' to heal your broken heart.

Quote of the day
'Deny your weakness, and you will never realize God's strength in you.'[3] – Joni Eareckson Tada

Memory verse for the week

'My _____ is sufficient for you,

for my strength is made perfect in weakness.'

(2 Cor. 12:9)

Daily Journal

Tips for journeying together: Choosing your words
Listen to a hurting person and, identify the negative words
they are using – hurtful words, judging words, feeling words,
attacking words – and explore where they may have come from.

Sustaining and Strengthening Comfort

'And the God of all grace, who called you to his eternal glory in Christ, after you have suffered a little while, will himself restore you and make you strong, firm and steadfast. To him be the power for ever and ever. Amen.' **(1 Pet. 5:10–11, NIV)**

I read the story of a Paralympian whose tyre blew out near the end of a wheelchair marathon. He kept going on the rim of his wheel, until, not far from the finish line, the wheel eventually buckled and the chair fell over. Some people on the sidelines ran and held the chair level running alongside, journeying with him while he finished the race. It was not their sympathy or empathy that got him to the finish line, but their applied strength.

There is a difference between the words 'sympathy', 'empathy' and 'comfort'. Over the past few weeks, we have seen that *sympathy* is subjective, it gets down into the valley of trouble and says, 'I am truly sorry for what you are going through'. *Empathy* is more objective, it gets down into the valley of trouble and says, 'I sense and feel something of your pain, and what you are going through'. But *comfort* is providing strength and support. It is amative, it gets down into the valley of trouble and says, 'I identify with what you are going through, I will provide practical love and strength to help you pick yourself up and dust yourself down, to then continue on your journey'.

So what does 'amative' mean? Coming from the Latin word for 'amorous', it is the impartation of love to another, with all of its restorative strength and qualities. Philippians 2:1 (GNB) says, 'Your life in Christ makes you strong, and his love comforts you.' Comfort means identifying with a person's circumstances, understanding what is going on in their heart, and pouring in strength and consolation. 'For we have great joy and consolation in your love, because the hearts of the saints have been refreshed by you' (Philem. 1:7).

Many of us will have seen a small child fall, bruise and cut their knee, burst into floods of tears, only for their mother to then scoop them up, put her healing lips on the poorly knee to 'kiss it better' and the floods of tears quickly dry up. Almost instantly, the child is on their way again without a care in the world, the knee healing, the fall almost forgotten. This is a mother's amative comfort at work.

Just like the Paralympian's tyre, life has its blowouts. Sometimes we buckle under its pressure, and need friends from the sidelines to journey with us to give us comfort and strength. Comfort never completely dismisses the pain but brings the balm of love to a wounded soul. People often respond wrongly to life's situations but when the strengthening power of amative comfort is ministered by others, then every setback can be turned into a springboard.

Quote of the day
'God does not comfort us to make us comfortable, but to make us comforters.'[4] – J. H. Jowett

Memory verse for the week

'My grace is _____ for you, for my strength is made perfect in weakness.'
(2 Cor. 12:9)

Daily Journal

Tips for journeying together: Choosing your words
List words of affirmation that people have used that have
blessed and encouraged you. Do you use these words enough
to bless and affirm others?

Forgiving the Debt

'Bear with each other and forgive one another if any of you has a grievance against someone. Forgive as the Lord forgave you.' **(Col. 3:13, NIV)**

Life deals blows to us all, but those who meet life with the right responses are those who turn their weaknesses into strengths. If we fail to respond to God's grace, we are more likely to suffer a life blighted by bitterness. Ephesians 4:31 indicates that bitterness doesn't stand alone, but brings a large family with it, such as 'wrath and anger and clamour and slander … [and] malice' (ESV). Wrath is exploding rage, anger is imploding rage, clamour is an old fashioned word for temper tantrums, slander is blaming others, and malice is the desire to hurt someone else. These are often acts of wounded retaliation. As Mahatma Gandhi observed, 'An eye for an eye makes the whole world blind.'[5]

The antidote to bitterness is not getting even, but being forgiven. 'Christ … is your example. Follow in his steps … when he suffered he did not threaten to get even; he left his case in the hands of God who always judges fairly' (1 Pet. 2:21–23, TLB).

Bitterness arises from the belief that the perpetrator owes us and must somehow pay us back – like a debt that must be paid, and if they can't be made to pay, someone else should. The truth of the matter is, the perpetrator may not pay, we the victim cannot pay, but the innocent recipients of the subsequent bitterness and anger, pay a heavy price in our resentment towards another. Jesus put it in context when He spoke of forgiveness in terms of releasing a person from a debt we perceive they owe us: 'And forgive us our debts, as we also have forgiven our debtors' (Matt. 6:12, ASV). Jesus says that to forgive means to choose to release the person from that debt, as we have been released from our debt. We cannot overcome what we will not confront. We need to admit to being wounded and hurt, recognising the debt cannot always be paid, but it can be forgiven.

What then is forgiveness? Forgiveness means writing off a debt. We are all human and when someone hurts us it is sometimes easy to want justice or revenge, but God is responsible for justice, not us. 'Don't hit back; discover beauty in everyone. If you've got it in you, get along with everybody. Don't insist on getting even; that's not for you to do. "I'll do the judging," says God. "I'll take care of it"' (Rom 12:19, *The Message*). If we want to be released, we must release those who have hurt and mistreated us, releasing them into God's hands. How can we do that? Our verse today shows the starting point: 'Forgive as the Lord forgave you.' Until we fully comprehend how much we are forgiven and experience the overwhelming release of knowing our immense debt of sin has been fully paid, it will be hard to forgive others. When we deserved judgment, God showed us mercy. The glorious message of the cross is that our debt has been paid in full: 'Think of it! All sins forgiven, the slate wiped clean, that old arrest warrant canceled and nailed to Christ's Cross' (Col. 2:14, *The Message*). The hymn writer Horatio Spafford (1873) wrote:

> *My sin, oh, the bliss of this glorious thought!*
> *My sin, not in part but the whole,*
> *Is nailed to the cross, and I bear it no more,*
> *Praise the Lord, praise the Lord, O my soul!*
> *... It is well, it is well with my soul.*[6]

Remember: grace takes the blame, covers the shame and removes the stain.

Quote of the day
'To forgive is to set a prisoner free and discover that the prisoner was you.'[7] – Lewis B. Smedes

Memory verse for the week

'My grace is sufficient _____ _____,

my strength is made perfect in weakness.'

(2 Cor. 12:9)

Daily Journal

(blank lined journal area)

Tips for journeying together: Choosing your words
Our well meaning words can be overshadowed by strong
perfume, aftershave or our slovenly appearance. As well as
thinking about the most helpful words to use, remember that
when you come alongside someone it is also important to be
aware of your personal hygiene and how you dress.

Forgiveness Frames the Future

'For I know the plans I have for you, says the Lord. They are plans for good and not for evil, to give you a future and a hope.' **(Jer. 29:11, TLB)**

Forgiveness is so seminal to becoming strong at the broken places that we need to spend another day considering it together. Unforgiveness incarcerates, it never rehabilitates. Forgiveness liberates our soul and frames our future – a healing journey that enables us to escape from what was and to embrace what is, moving positively forward to what can be. Without forgiveness, there really is no future.

We said yesterday, forgiveness means writing off a debt once and for all. So how do we move forward? Now let's be clear, forgiveness does not necessarily *condone* – it is not approval of wrong behaviour or what a person did. It also does not *deny* – for some, the pain is too great to bear and they deny that anything has happened at all, it is their way of dulling the pain. Forgiveness does not *pretend* – when someone will not admit that they were hurt and claim everything is fine. And lastly, it does not *lose* – some feel that if they forgive, they are the loser and the other person the winner. Remember, forgiveness always wins out in the end.

Others say 'forgive and forget' but is that always possible? If the offence is small, maybe, but if it is big, you may never forget it, even when you forgive. Forgiveness does not always forget the past but by God's grace it nullifies its toxic memories and cuts off the tentacles of its pernicious influence.

Our goal is not only helping others to be released from the past, but to help them move on to the future. That means helping to rebuild trust, and that takes time. Rebuilding cannot be done on what has been lost. It begins when we recognise and appreciate what we have left.

Wounded people develop three relational positions:

- The insulator: Who protects themselves because of the fear that what happened in the past will inevitably happen again. They have a battered heart that won't let others in.

- The isolator: Who separates themselves so as to avoid the possibility of suffering rejection again. They have a bruised spirit that doesn't want to risk further damage.

- The inhibitor: Who becomes timid and fainthearted. They carry a deep sense of a lack of self-worth, identity and value. They have a damaged self-image.

Journeying with others on the pathway of forgiveness, and helping them move on from these relational positions, is part of the healing process. It is a road of recovery. *Reassure* them that having taken the step of forgiveness they have no need to occupy any of these life positions any more. *Affirm* that they are better than the worst things they have ever done, or that they have ever had done to them; the slate is wiped clean through forgiveness. *Confirm* that they are not what they once were, but are recipients of God's grace; His unmerited favour. *Assure* them that through forgiveness, their battered heart will be healed, their broken spirit renewed, their damaged image restored.

Quote of the day

'You must write off the past, so that you are available for the future. You can't drive forward with your eyes fixed on the rear view mirror.'[8] – Bishop T D Jakes

Memory verse for the week

'My grace is sufficient for you, for my

_____ is made perfect in

weakness.' (2 Cor. 12:9)

Daily Journal

_____

_____

_____

_____

_____

_____

_____

_____

_____

_____

_____

_____

_____

_____

_____

_____

_____

Tips for journeying together: Choosing your words
When communicating with someone who may have had a
different background to you, be considerate of their language
and vocabulary level. Try not to talk down to them, patronise
them or try to impress them with your own understanding
and skill with words. Listen to the words they use and
communicate with them at their level of understanding.

Responders or Reactors

'We are handicapped on all sides, but we are never frustrated; we are puzzled, but never in despair. We are persecuted, but we never have to stand it alone: we may be knocked down but we are never knocked out!' **(2 Cor. 4:8–9, Phillips)**

This week, we have seen that the biblical response to all of life's struggles is to take advantage of the unfailing grace of God, and to forgive as we have been forgiven. Some will respond by saying, 'It sounds good in theory, but it's hard to put it into practice. What about the hurts that some people carry inside them, that make it difficult or sometimes impossible for them to avail themselves of God's grace?' Having personally sat in a pastoral seat for many years now, I recognise that the wounds some people carry run deep and long, and seem to overwhelm their desire to respond to life in a biblical way. However, we have seen that God allows nothing to happen to one of His children without supplying a corresponding source of grace to turn the stumbling block into a stepping-stone, the setback into a springboard.

I know unconditional forgiveness is a tall order, but if Christianity is about anything it is about forgiveness. God never calls on us to do what we are incapable of doing. He sets the standards high but promises to supply a corresponding source of grace to enable us to reach them. There is no small print with forgiveness in the Bible. Forgiveness means forgiveness. I know of no other way to be free of bitterness, anger, resentment, guilt or to receive healing for a wounded spirit, than to take the courage to follow the biblical way of grace and forgiveness.

Some Christians believe they should be exempt from the cruel blows of life but when God allows what appears to be a disaster into our lives, be assured He can turn it to good effect, and use it as part of our transformation journey. So let this truth sink deep into your spirit, as He calls us to draw on His mercy, grace and forgiveness, whether we feel like it or not.

I know myself that in my own human weakness there are times when I am prone to react to a situation rather than to turn to God for His grace.

WEEK 5
HEALING

I know, however, what is right, that God has offered a supply of His grace freely in Jesus, that I need to trust Him, turn to Him, draw on that grace and do what He wants me to do: forgive, whether I feel like it or not. The choice is mine.

We can face our weaknesses in the assurance that, no matter how life breaks us, God's strength is sufficient to help us to recover and be overcomers. Although some of the same things may happen to each of us, they do not have the same effect on all of us. Life's blows make some people bitter, others better. Grace makes the difference. What matters, therefore, is not so much what happens to us but what we do with it.

Quote of the day

'Bitterness or joylessness in suffering happens when we've held on to something more than we've held on to God.'[9]
– Tullian Tchividjian

Memory verse for the week

'My grace is sufficient for you, for my strength is made _____ in weakness.'
(2 Cor. 12:9)

Daily Journal

_____

_____

_____

_____

_____

_____

_____

_____

_____

_____

_____

_____

_____

_____

_____

_____

_____

Tips for journeying together: Choosing your words
Often, the best thing you can say to someone is, 'I may not be able to help, but I am ready to listen and I care.' If they decline, respect their wish and express your concern and support by continuing to be there for them, if they change their minds.

Review

Think back over this week, the sermon content, the daily readings and the memory verse. You could read your Daily Journal entries to refresh your memory of each day. Now jot down one or more comments under the questions below:

· What more have I learnt about God this week?

· What have I learnt about others this week?

· What have I learnt about myself this week?

JOURNEYING TOGETHER ACTION PLAN

How are you finding journeying with the people you have connected with? Are there any new ways in which you can interact and engage with them? Journal here how you can develop your journey in the last week of *Paraclesis: Journeying Together* and implement some of the tips you have learnt so far.

My journey with others:

- Church family:

  _____

- Local community/work colleagues:

  _____

Prayer

Gracious Father, teach me the art of responding to life through the perspective of Your grace. I ask that this truth be so indelibly imprinted on my spirit that I will always be open to receive Your never-ending supply of grace. Amen.

Memory verse for the week

'My grace is sufficient for you, for my strength is made perfect in _____.'
(2 Cor. 12:9)

NOTES

As you prepare to start week six of this series, you may want to note down what you have learnt so far and anything you would like to focus on in your last week ...

WEEK 6
Connecting

'I want you to get out there and walk – better yet, run! – on the road God called you to travel. I don't want any of you sitting around on your hands. I don't want anyone strolling off, down some path that goes nowhere. And mark that you do this with humility and discipline – not in fits and starts, but steadily, pouring yourselves out for each other in acts of love'
(Eph. 4:1–3, *The Message*)

Have You Ever Felt the Need?

The Man at the Gate Beautiful – Acts 3:1–10

Caring by connecting

'Each one of us needs to look after the good of the people around us, asking ourselves, "How can I help?"'
(Rom. 15:2, *The Message*)

PARAKALEO – TO ENTREAT

*'And he was angry, and would not go in: therefore came his father out, and intreated [**parakaleo**] him'*
(Luke 15:28, KJV)

> ENTREAT: To approach, reach out, connect, draw close and engage with others at the point of felt need; persuading and pleading.

Jesus gave the disciples three clear directives:

- The Great Commission (Matt. 28:19–20)
- The Great Command (John 13:34; 15:12)
- The Great Connection (John 20:21–22)

Engaging with felt needs

'God's Way is not a matter of mere talk; it's an empowered life.' **(1 Cor. 4:20, *The Message*)**

PARAKLETOS – ONE WHO COMES ALONGSIDE

Jesus engaged with people's felt needs:

The felt need is the _____ need

Jesus _____ felt needs

Felt need leads to _____ needs

Connecting to the real needs

This man was:

_____ by religion

_____ on others

This was a day of opportunity. Peter and John were connected:

To a _____ community

With the _____ man

With his _____ need

To his _____ need

Sharing your gift of journey

'*such as I have I give thee.*' **(Acts 3:6, KJV)**

Don't look at what you _____ _____

Realise what you _____ _____

Embrace it with _____

You have a _____ _____

_____

Empowered in Jesus' name

'*In the name of Jesus Christ of Nazareth, rise up and walk.*'
(Acts 3:6)

• They gave him a hand-up not a hand-out

• They grasped the connecting opportunity

• They engaged in journey evangelism

Who Cares? Do You Care? We Care!

Sermon Notes

Do You Care?

"'I was hungry and you gave me something to eat ... thirsty and you gave me something to drink .... a stranger and you invited me in ... needed clothes and you clothed me ... ill and you looked after me ... in prison and you came to visit me." Then the righteous will answer ... "When ... ?" ... The King will reply, "Truly I tell you, whatever you did for one of the least of these brothers and sisters of mine, you did for me."'
(Matt. 25:35—40, NIV)

Have you ever asked yourself the question, 'Who cares?' I wonder if your response has been, 'I do'. This is what our text today underlines, to be aware of the needs of others around us. When we choose not to look at the need, we can walk past, and every time we walk past it becomes easier until we don't notice anymore. The question I want to put to you today is how aware are you of others? How conscious are you of those who are pressed down with deep, perplexing struggles? Have you a genuine concern for people in trouble? Are you mindful of their felt needs? A developed sense of awareness is the key to involvement. Martin Luther once said, 'Good works do not make a good man, but a good man does good works.'[1]

During the Second World War, Bob Pierce visited a missionary school near Tibet. On the steps leading into the school, sat a small ragged girl with sad eyes called White Jade. Her short lifetime had been one of suffering and hardship. He asked the teacher why she wasn't in class that day. The teacher Tena Hoelkeboer replied that she sat there every day wanting to attend, but the class was already overflowing and there was no room for her. Troubled, Bob Pierce asked, 'Can't you make room for one more?' The teacher replied, 'I've made room for one more too often, food is stretched to the absolute limit, and I have to draw a line somewhere.' Bob Pierce indignantly exclaimed, 'No child who wants to be in class should be turned away – why is nothing being done?' The teacher quietly picked up the little girl and put her in his arms, replying, 'What are you going to do about it?'

That day Bob Pierce reached into his pocket, handed her $5 and said 'If you'll take care of her, I'll send more when I get home.'[2]

That one act led to the founding of World Vision International, which today raises around £2 billion for humanitarian aid, sponsoring millions of children in poverty into education, child protection, health care and providing nutritious food in countries around the globe. Later, Bob founded The Samaritan's Purse. When asked by Franklin Graham how to 'shake people out of their complacency', Pierce said he had 'become a part of the suffering. I literally felt the child's blindness, the mother's grief.'[3]

Pastor Richard Halvorsen wrote, 'Bob Pierce functioned from a broken heart.'[4] In answer to the question 'Who cares?' on that day, Bob Pierce responded to the felt need, 'I do'.

Although we may feel that in our nature we are not caring people, we must live in such close relationship with Jesus Christ that His concerns become our concerns, His sensitivity becomes our sensitivity, His interests become our interests. His primary concern is people. In today's verses, Jesus said when you reach out to 'the hungry ... the thirsty ... the stranger ... the naked ... the sick ... the prisoner' you do so for Him. Today, put your hand in His hand, then reach out and take hold of the hand of someone in need.

Quote of the day
'Let my heart be broken with the things that break the heart of God.'[5] – Bob Pierce

Memory verse for the week

'A _____ Samaritan ... came where he was. And when he saw him, he had compassion. So he went to him ... and took care of him.' (Luke 10:33–34)

Daily Journal

_____

_____

_____

_____

_____

_____

_____

_____

_____

_____

_____

_____

_____

_____

_____

_____

_____

Tips for journeying together: Be a reflector
Feeding back to a person what they are sharing with you helps them to know that you are understanding what they are saying, and gives them the opportunity to correct anything that you may have misheard or misunderstood.

Humanising God

'The Voice took on flesh and became human *and chose to live alongside us. We have seen Him, enveloped in undeniable splendor – the one* true *Son of the Father* – evidenced in *the perfect balance of grace and truth.'* **(John 1:14, TV)**

Yesterday we touched on the fact that when we choose not to look at the need, we can walk past, and every time we walk past, it becomes easier until we don't notice anymore. The beggar at the temple gate called Beautiful had been there for many years. Many walked by, insensitive, unconcerned, even Peter and John had undoubtedly walked past him before. He was always at the gate when they went to church. But on this day, they stopped, gazed at him and engaged with his felt need. This day, they would become the tangible expression of Christ's compassion and their deeds would become as good as their doctrines.

Closer to home, a pastor gathered a group from his church to train them to witness. After some minimal training, he sent them out into the locality. When they returned to share their experiences, one young man said he had tried to tell an older gentleman about the love of Jesus. The old gentleman replied, 'I feel none of the love of God. I feel nothing of God caring for my burdens. I am old and must take care of myself, shop for myself, and carry my groceries home from the shops, by myself.' One of the group remarked, 'Perhaps if you had offered to carry his load for him, he would have believed your words because he would have experienced them first-hand in you.' To this old man, the young man's gospel didn't count because he didn't first take time to understand and recognise his felt need. He missed it, and in that moment lost an opportunity.

In Madras, India, a missionary addressing an audience told them that the ultimate image of caring is the picture of God upon a cross. He said, 'The God we see in Jesus is a God who cares, cares enough to give Himself on a cross.' After finishing his address, the chairman, who was a Hindu doctor, arose and said, 'We appreciate this moving address, but we must not involve God in the affairs of this world. He is lifted above all these things.

We must not humanise God.' This is the basic belief of a deist. This man had failed to read our verse for today. To him, his god was a god who was impervious and insensitive to the human condition, a distant disengaged being who didn't care. But a god who doesn't care, doesn't count. A god who would sit in awful isolation, separated and uninvolved with his creation, is not worth considering. Despite the statement of the Hindu doctor that 'we must not involve God in the affairs of this world', the Almighty has, by His own volition, entered through the door of humanity and involved Himself with us in the person of His Son, Jesus Christ. His involvement is our involvement, and we must now involve ourselves with others.

Now it's up to us to 'humanise God' and like Peter and John at the Beautiful Gate, seize a moment today to be a channel of His tender, loving mercies to others.

Quote of the day

'If you cannot feed a hundred people, then feed just one.'[6]
– Mother Theresa

Memory verse for the week

'A certain _____ ... came where he was. And when he saw him, he had compassion. So he went to him ... and took care of him.' (Luke 10:33–34)

Daily Journal

_____

_____

_____

_____

_____

_____

_____

_____

_____

_____

_____

_____

_____

_____

_____

_____

_____

_____

Tips for journeying together: Be a reflector
Reflecting back accurately not only helps a person feel you
are genuinely interested in them, but it also gives them
an opportunity to add something they may have missed,
clarifying things for them.

WEEK 6
CONNECTING

Fly a Kite and Build a Bridge

'Share each other's troubles and problems, and so obey our Lord's command. If anyone thinks he is too great to stoop to this, he is fooling himself. He is really a nobody.'
(Gal. 6:2–3, TLB)

Peter and John said, 'such as I have I give thee' (Acts 3:6, KJV). Often, we don't think our 'such' is enough, but what they didn't have didn't stop them reaching out. One reason we are reticent to engage is because we think that we will not be able to meet the need. We reason, 'if I can't do it right, I won't do it at all'. We hold back, thinking others' needs are greater than our resources – that reaching out to a felt need will be too costly. Our concern is that, in meeting another's needs, we may even become needy ourselves, and this is not worth taking the risk. But if we are not willing to take the risk with the things that we can give, even if it is not much, we will never get off the starting block. Almost anything that is done in life is done falteringly at first.

I wonder how many times you fell over when you started to walk. That's how we learn. Even the best people don't get it right at first. It may be pride that holds us back – too proud to dirty our hands. Jesus embraced the bowl and towel ministry, stooped down and washed the feet of His disciples (John 13:4–10). Today's text says, 'If anyone thinks he is too great to stoop to this, he is fooling himself, he is really a nobody.' Much of Jesus' ministry was spent tearing down old barriers and building new bridges through acts of love, washing the feet of those who would betray Him, deny Him, doubt Him and forsake Him.

In 1848, Charles Ellet, an American engineer, looked across the Niagara River Gorge, near the Falls where 37.4 million gallons of water thundered down. He dared to think that the chasm, 200 feet deep and 820 feet wide, a swirling rushing cauldron of water, could be spanned. Naysayers predicted disaster and failure.

Not to be deterred, he started to figure out how he could reach across the divide. How could he make the initial connect and get a wire across this gaping dangerous span? He organised a kite competition offering a $5 reward to the first boy who could fly a kite so high he could land it on the other side of the chasm. The first and second day, nobody succeeded, but on the third, Homan Walsh won the prize. The string of the kite was tied to a tree, a light chord attached, and slowly pulled back across the gorge. Next a heavier one, then a rope, and finally a cable of 10-strand wire. This was the beginning of Ellet's Niagara Falls Suspension Bridge that joins America to Canada.[7]

You see, not everyone can build a bridge but everyone can fly a kite, and if you don't fly a kite, you may never build a bridge. Your 'such' may only seem like a kite but if you're willing to fly it, God will catch it on the wind of His Spirit and it can be the beginning of a bridge over which many can cross.

Quote of the day

'Do all the good you can. By all the means you can. In all the ways you can. In all the places you can. At all the times you can. To all the people you can. As long as ever you can.'[8] – John Wesley

Memory verse for the week

'A certain Samaritan ... came where he was.

And when _____ _____ _____,

he had compassion. So he went to him ...

and took care of him.' (Luke 10:33–34)

Daily Journal

_____

_____

_____

_____

_____

_____

_____

_____

_____

_____

_____

_____

_____

_____

_____

_____

_____

_____

_____

_____

_____

_____

Tips for journeying together: Be a reflector

Try to be more aware of how you respond to someone's facial expressions. If someone is depressed, don't grin like a Cheshire cat, but respond with a reassuring nod and gentle smile. If someone says something surprising, don't throw up your hands in horror; try and respond with a calm and composed expression.

A Story to Tell

'Your very lives are a letter that anyone can read by just looking at you. Christ himself wrote it – not with ink, but with God's living Spirit; not chiseled into stone, but carved into human lives – and we publish it' **(2 Cor. 3:2–3, *The Message*)**

Each of us who has encountered Jesus Christ has a story to tell. It's a story about how His grace has been part of our journey. Our journey, the journey of life, is one of the greatest gifts we have been given. You may say, 'But I was raised in the church, I don't have a dramatic testimony', but it doesn't matter if you don't have a dramatic testimony. Your life's journey is the story of the working of Jesus Christ in all of the circumstances of your life since you met Him. That makes it important and exciting. You may say, 'But I don't have much to offer' or 'I'm nobody special'. Well, Jesus thinks you are special enough to die for and He is part of your journey. You can't tell me that if the Creator of the universe values you so much, that your story and journey has no relevance.

A woman once put an ad in the local paper: 'Lost 50 pounds! Selling my old clothes; they're in good condition, sizes 18–20.' She was bombarded with phone calls, but nobody wanted to buy the clothes, they all wanted to know how she had lost the 50 pounds! You see, the callers wanted to know about something that changed her life, hoping that this something could change their lives too. They wanted to hear her story, not buy her clothes. Our verse today says, 'Your very lives are a letter that anyone can read by just looking at you.'

Perhaps you've been told that you're no good. Perhaps your employer thinks you don't have potential. Perhaps your parents told you you'd never amount to much. Maybe someone rejected you or spurned your love. Well hear me on this, your story is important. You can be in no doubt about the direction that God wants you to go and what the Creator's highest purpose for your life is. It is receiving God's love, and then channelling that love into the lives of those around us who are struggling, weak and wounded. Reaching out to people at the point of their felt need, lifting the fallen, cheering the fainthearted, giving hope to the hopeless and reaching out to others on their journeys.

On the way home from church, a little girl said, 'Mum, I've been thinking.' The mother said, 'Oh, about what?' She replied, 'Well, this morning my teacher said God is bigger than we are. Is that true?' 'Yes, that's true,' the mother replied. 'He also said that God lives within us. Is that true too?' Again the mother replied, 'Yes,' 'Well,' said the girl. 'If God is bigger than us and He lives in us, wouldn't He show through?'

You and I need to ask ourselves, does Jesus show through our lives? He will when we take time to connect someone's story with our story, sharing *His* story with them.

Quote of the day
'You can preach a better sermon with your life than with your lips.'[9]
– Oliver Goldsmith

Memory verse for the week

'A certain Samaritan ... came where he was.

And when he saw him, he had _____ .

So he went to him ... and took care of him.'

(Luke 10:33–34)

Daily Journal

_____

_____

_____

_____

_____

_____

_____

_____

_____

_____

_____

_____

_____

_____

_____

_____

Tips for journeying together: Be a reflector

Feeding back can be about verbalising to the other person, using their own words. Stressing not only what they are saying, but also what you hear them expressing, including any underlying feelings that they may not be recognising or articulating. To understand people we must try and hear what they are not saying.

We Care!

> *"'As the Father has sent me, so I am sending you." Then he breathed on them and said, "Receive the Holy Spirit."'*
> **(John 20:21, NLT)**

Jesus, now risen from the dead, appears to His disciples. He tells them, 'As the Father has sent me, so I am sending you'. In other words: 'as I have come from the Father and been empowered to journey with people, to live and tell my story, to deeply impact and change lives, so I now empower you, and send you to do the same'. Someone has described this as the 'Divine Equation': As = So. *As* He came alongside and cared and connected; *So* He sends us to do the same. Christ is no longer bodily present on the earth. After His death and resurrection, He returned to His Father in heaven. The New Testament teaches that, today, Christ is now bodily present in the lives, words and loving deeds of His disciples, as He dwells in you and me.

This has been described as the extension of Christ – 'the second Incarnation' as expressed through the lives of His followers. Just as in the first Incarnation, God came in the person of His Son, Jesus Christ, to show humanity that He cared, so in the second Incarnation (His divine indwelling in His Church), He is present in the world to spell out that same wondrous message – God cares. It was said of Him that He 'went around doing good and healing all who were under the power of the devil, because God was with him' (Acts 10:38, NIV).

In my experience, thirty years ago, most people asked, 'Is the gospel true?' They wanted to be convinced of its veracity. Fifteen years ago they asked, 'Does the gospel work?' They wanted to see the proof of its relevance. Now people ask, 'Will the gospel meet my need today?' They want to feel the impact of the gospel at the point of their felt needs.

We used to ask, 'Where will you spend eternity?' but our post-modern generation are often not so interested in eternity. Sometimes it seems as if we can't even cope with today, let alone tomorrow. They cry out,

'Help me with my need today – my marriage breakdown, my bereavement, my redundancy, my daily struggle.' People more than ever are seeking someone to connect with at the point of felt need, to build a bridge to them, to come alongside them, to relate to their journey, to recount an authentic story of grace and truth. This is your divine purpose.

When Jesus commissioned these disciples to go and be a blessing to others, they were not the finished article or perfect men, but He sent them out warts and all with a story to tell and a journey to share. I heard of a charity official who, when asked about the secret to his organisation's success, answered, 'We see a need, we pray about it and we do something about it.'

Generally speaking, the climate in today's Church, is: we see a need, we pray about it, then we just discuss it. How sad is that when Jesus has said, 'As the Father has sent me, so I am sending you'? Some of us only open our churches one day a week to have a religious service instead of opening them seven days a week as a service to all who are in need, every day. So as we come to the end of this *Paraclesis: Journeying Together* study, this is the challenge: will you respond with your church, not simply in saying 'yes we care', but by actively going outside its four walls and caring by connecting?

Quote of the day

'It is time for us to put our love into action. Imagine what would happen if every small group in your church reached out together, showing love in practical ways to those in your community. Don't you think that would make a difference in your area?'[10]
– Rick Warren

Memory verse for the week

'A certain Samaritan ... came where he was.
And when he saw him, he had compassion.
So he _____ to him ... and took care of him.'
(Luke 10:33–34)

Daily Journal

_____

_____

_____

_____

_____

_____

_____

_____

_____

_____

_____

_____

_____

_____

_____

_____

_____

_____

_____

_____

Tips for journeying together: Be a reflector

When you feed back to someone a summary of what they
have said to you, it demonstrates immediacy – that is, that you
are identifying with what is important to them in the here and
now. It is being present with them in the moment, connecting
with the felt need rather than listening to and discussing an
account of the past. A question to ask is: 'How does this affect
you now?'

Review

Think back over this week, the sermon content, the daily readings and the memory verse. You could read your Daily Journal entries to refresh your memory of each day. Now jot down one or more comments under the questions below:

· What more have I learnt about God this week?

· What have I learnt about others this week?

· What have I learnt about myself this week?

JOURNEYING TOGETHER ACTION PLAN

How have you got on with your action plan over the six weeks? There will have been a number of people you will intentionally have connected with during *Paraclesis: Journeying Together*. You may need to journey with some of them for a little while. Give some thought to this, and make a note below of who and how you intend to continue to journey together.

- Church family:

  _____

- Local community/work colleagues:

  _____

Prayer

Loving Father, as I come to the close of this series, and face the challenge and opportunity of the highest reason for my existence, to be Your love with skin on, help me not to turn from it, afraid of the responsibility, but embrace it in Your strength. For in doing so I know I will be walking with true purpose. Amen.

Memory verse for the week

'A certain Samaritan ... came where he was. And when he saw him, he had compassion. So he went to him ... and _____ _____ of him.' (Luke 10:33–34)

The gift of your journey

'He comes alongside us when we go through hard times, and before you know it, He brings us alongside someone else who is going through hard times, so that we can be there for that person just as God was there for us.' **(2 Cor. 1:4, *The Message*)**

Every person has a story to tell. We have all journeyed, in some way, through certain life experiences and challenges. And these experiences not only shape us personally but we can use them to come alongside someone who is facing a similar challenge in their journey – reaching out to them with our knowledge of God's grace and compassion (just as 2 Cor. 1:4 explains). This life experience is our resource. It is an invaluable gift that we can offer to others. It is a gift of encouragement, understanding and insight – we know how they feel and we might have the key to help them through, in their walk with God.

It's quite possible that you have kept your gift tightly wrapped, placed out of sight or buried in your past. This resource can remain 'untapped' unless we take the time to look back and reflect on our own journey so far. By identifying what we have experienced – physically, mentally, emotionally and spiritually – and recognising the grace, truth and goodness of God in our lives, we can move forward as a fellow travellers with confidence and purpose. We can share our experiences with others by coming alongside them.

The next few pages will help you identify your own gift – the gift of your journey. In this exercise you will be completing eight sections that identify different aspects of your journey. The following examples are not exhaustive. They are simply included to help clarify the sections, as well as help you recall and pinpoint details of your past experiences.

Before you read these, take a few moments to pray, inviting the Holy Spirit to come and help bring valuable parts of your journey to the surface.

Examples of significant life events or circumstances

Bereavement	Relocation	Homelessness
Redundancy	Disability	Abuse
Divorce	Failing a qualification	Bullying
Sickness	Singleness	Addiction
A serious accident	Childlessness	Infidelity
Financial setback	Mental illness	

Struggles experienced

Failure	Stress	Confusion
Rejection	Shame	Despair
Disappointment	Disillusionment	Loneliness
Guilt	Anger	Unforgiveness

Core beliefs and values developed

Identity	Trust	Confidence
Self-worth	Purpose	Future
Security	Priorities	
Belonging	Focus	

Challenges faced

Mobility	Relationships	Family
Financial difficulty	Personal struggle	Emotional swings
Health	Thought patterns	Choices
Time management	Career	Indecisiveness

Change moments

Encounter with God

Came to faith

Encouragement from another person

Practical help

A resonant Bible verse or passage

Core belief/value realigned with God

A new insight or perspective

Hearing a particular sermon or worship song

Applied grace and truth

God's faithfulness

God's love

God's provision

Forgiveness

Freedom

Being 'made new'

Hope restored

Ongoing challenges

Lack of justice

Temptation

Broken relationship

Repaying debt

Family issues

Work pressures

Spiritual disciplines

Financial security

Physical health

Meaningful outcomes

Relationship with God

Bible reading

Prayer life

Resilience to circumstances

Faith

Character

Personal growth

Restored relationships

Sense of purpose

Gratitude for God's goodness

Insights for living

Peace and contentment

On the following page is a diagram to help you jot down an overview of your journey, highlighting the different stages we may experience after a significant life event or circumstance.

Write down a significant life event or circumstance, or several, in the space provided. Then follow the 'My Journey' line and under each of the headings, jot down your responses, using significant words or brief descriptions. Once completed, you will have a basic overview to help you identify important aspects in your personal journey.

SIGNIFICANT LIFE EVENT OR CIRCUMSTANCE

For example: my father's early death _____

Struggles experienced

Abandonment _____

_____

_____

_____

Challenges faced

Mistrust others _____

_____

_____

_____

My Journey

LIFE TIMELINE

Core beliefs and values developed

People fail me _____

_____

_____

_____

Change moments

Attending a church _____

conference on grief _____

_____

_____

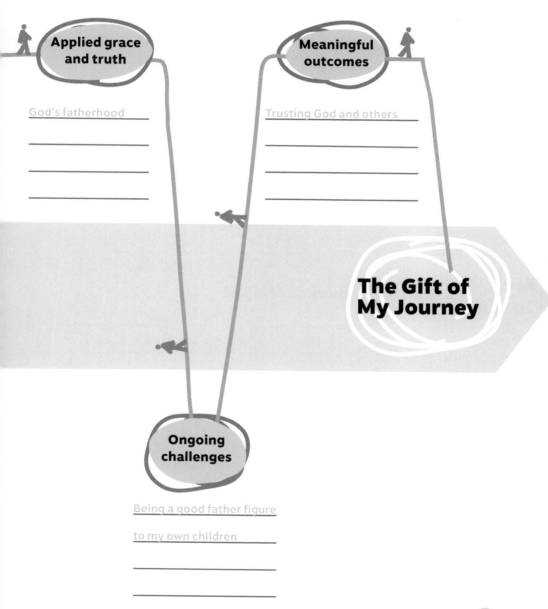

Applied grace and truth

God's fatherhood

Meaningful outcomes

Trusting God and others

The Gift of My Journey

Ongoing challenges

Being a good father figure

to my own children

Now that you've filled in the diagram, here's some extra space for you to expand on your own journey story, based on the overview you have just completed.

You might like to copy the headings out into a journal or notebook so that you can complete the exercise for multiple life events or circumstances.

Significant life event or circumstance

_____

Struggles experienced

_____

_____

_____

_____

Core beliefs and values developed

_____

_____

_____

_____

Challenges faced

_____

_____

_____

_____

Change moments

_____

_____

_____

_____

Applied grace and truth

_____

_____

_____

_____

Ongoing challenges

_____

_____

_____

_____

Meaningful outcomes

_____

_____

_____

_____

Sharing the gift of my journey with others

Looking at the example on the diagram, the person suffering from the early death of their father faced certain struggles and challenges, but through moments of change and applied grace and truth, they managed to reach meaningful outcomes. They now have a gift to offer others who may be experiencing bereavement.

You too should now have an overview of your story and details of your life experiences. You have, therefore, identified the aspects that make up the gift of your journey!

So, what next? It's time to start looking for opportunities to share your gift with those it could greatly benefit – and start journeying together.

Sharing our stories, and journeying with each other, not only helps others but it helps us better understand our experiences ourselves. There is a principle that expression deepens impression, that is to say that often it's not until we begin to share something in detail with another that events and situations fall into an even greater perspective and understanding for us. This can be a very enriching, rewarding and meaningful experience.

Each of us who has come to Christ has a story to tell – a journey of grace, mercy, truth, forgiveness, and the goodness of God, to share. Yours is an individual story of what God has done in your life, it has relevance for others, and it is worth telling. So begin to look for the opportunities to come alongside and journey with others today! Bear this in mind when you complete your journey card at the end of this series.

A note for small groups

It is helpful to begin to share your stories when you meet in your small midweek groups during the Paraclesis: Journeying Together series. You could sensitively encourage members to bring their *Daily Guide* and share parts of their story (if willing and suitable). This provides the opportunity for the group to grow closer and more aware of each other – being better equipped to journey together as a small group as well as a church.

Endnotes

Week 1

[1] From Martin Luther King Jr's speech 'I've been to the mountaintop', delivered in Memphis, 3 April 1968. A full recording from the speech can be found at [www.americanrhetoric.com/speeches/mlkivebeentothemountaintop.htm] (accessed March 2016).

[2] Author unknown; material found at [www.sermonillustrations.com/a-z/s/self_centered.htm] (accessed March 2016).

[3] Cited in Hannah Ward and Jennifer Wild (eds.), *The Lion Christian Quotation Collection* (Oxford, England: Lion Publishing, 1997).

[4] E. Stanley Jones, 'Abundant Living for You' (article), *The Tuscaloosa News* (AL, USA: 15 February 1950). Article found at [news.google.com/newspapers?nid=1817&dat=19500215&id=jvQ-AAAAIBAJ&sjid=WE0MAAAAIBAJ&pg=2264,3322030&hl=en] (accessed March 2016).

[5] Author unknown, some attribute this to Oscar Wilde.

[6] John Powell, *Why Am I Afraid to Tell You Who I Am: Insights into Personal Growth* (Grand Rapids, MI, USA: Zondervan, 1999).

[7] John Powell, *Why I Am Afraid to Love* (IL, USA: Argus Communications, 1975), p78.

[8] Bede Griffiths, cited in Judson B. Trapnell, *Bede Griffiths: A Life in Dialogue* (Albany, NY, USA: State University of New York Press, 2001).

Week 2

[1] St Francis of Assisi, AD 1181–1226 (public domain).

[2] Anthony J. D'Angelo, found at [www.brainyquote.com/slideshow/authors/top_10_anthony_j_dangelo_quotes.html] (accessed March 2016).

[3] Richard Whately, cited in Joyce Meyer, *100 Ways to Simplify Your Life* (London: Hodder & Stoughton, 2007).

[4] Dr. Clyde Narramore, *Every Person is Worth Understanding* (Bloomington, IN, USA: CrossBooks, 2011).

[5] Joel Osteen, *Your Best Life Now: 7 Steps to Living at Your Full Potential* (Nashville, TN, USA: Faithwords, 2009).

[6] Jim Fuller, [www.pastoralcareinc.com/resources/sermon-helps/quotes-for-sermons/] (accessed March 2016).

[7] Pope Saint Gregory I, AD 540–604 (public domain).

Week 3

[1] Alex Elle, also known as Alexandra L. Smith [www.alexelle.info]. Found at [www.goodreads.com/quotes/1177779] (accessed March 2016).

[2] St Augustine of Hippo, AD 354–430 (public domain).

[3] St Francis of Assisi, AD 1181–1226 (public domain).

[4] Steve Maraboli, *Life, the Truth, and Being Free* (Port Washington, NY, USA: A Better Today Publishing, 2009).

[5] Hudson Taylor, cited in Richard Broadhurst, *Life's 'Answer': A Life Changing Message of Assurance and Challenge* (Milton Keynes, UK: AuthorHouse UK Ltd, 2012).

[6] Charles Spurgeon, from his sermon 'Consolation in Christ' (No. 348) delivered 2 December 1860 at Exeter Hall, Strand. See *The Complete Works of C.H. Spurgeon: Volume 7, Sermons 348–426* (USA: Delmarva Publications, 2013).

[7] Vance Havner, cited in *Grace for Each Day: 369 Devotions and Prayers* (Brentwood, TN, USA: Worthy Media, Inc., 2014).

[8] George Muller, cited in Dr. and Mrs. Howard Taylor, *Hudson Taylor's Spiritual Secret* (Chicago, IL, USA: Moody Publishers, 2009).

Week 4

[1] Joel Osteen, *Your Best Life Now: 7 Steps to Living at Your Full Potential* (Nashville, TN, USA: Faithwords, 2009).

[2] Article by Steve Doughty, 'I sometimes question if God exists: Archbishop of Canterbury admits he sometimes has moments of doubt' (17 September 2014) *The Daily Mail Online* (2016) found at [www.dailymail.co.uk/news/article-2760048/I-question-God-exists-Archbishop-Canterbury-admits-moments-doubt.html] (accessed March 2016).

[3] Henry Drummond, *The Greatest Thing in the World and Other Writings* (Nashville, TN, USA: Thomas Nelson, 2000).

[4] Article by Ned Smith, *The World Health Organisation* (28 March 2012). Found at [www.businessnewsdaily.com/2267-workplace-stress-health-epidemic-perventable-employee-assistance-programs.html] (accessed March 2016).

[4] From 'Stress Balls: Good for the Brain and Good for Business', *A Few Good Promos* (2016), found at [www.afewgoodpromos.com/tag/unique-stress-balls/] (accessed March 2016).

[6] Quotation attributed to Pastor Louie Giglio of Passion City Church, Georgia, USA. Found at [www.pinterest.com/shediupp/louie-giglio-quotes/] (accessed March 2016).

[7] John Wesley, AD 1703–1791 (public domain).

[8] Bradley Kellam, found at [www.sermoncentral.com/sermons/how-god-restores-our-losses-bradley-kellum-sermon-on-hardship-of-life-137941.asp?Page=6] (accessed March 2016).

Week 5

[1] Song lyrics by Chuck Girard. Used by permission. ©1982 Sea of Glass Music/ASCAP.

[2] Annie Dillard, *Teaching a Stone to Talk* (London: HarperCollins, 2009).

[3] Joni Eareckson Tada, *Ordinary People, Extraordinary Faith* (Nashville, TN, USA: Thomas Nelson, Inc., 2001).

[4] J.H. Jowett, cited in Hannah Ward and Jennifer Wild (eds.), *The Lion Christian Quotation Collection* (Oxford, England: Lion Publishing, 1997).

[5] Mahatma Gandhi, AD 1869–1948.

[6] Horatio Spafford, 'It is well with my soul', 1873 (hymn).

[7] Lewis B Smedes, *Forgive and Forget: Healing the Hurts We Don't Deserve* (San Francisco, USA: HarperOne, 1984).

[8] Bishop T.D. Jakes, *Let it Go: Forgive so You can be Forgiven* (New York, USA: Atria Books, 2012).

[9] Tullian Tchividjian, 'Trouble Happens: What Suffering Will Do for You', *The Road We Must Travel: A Personal Guide For Your Journey* (Franklin, TN, USA: Worthy Publishing, 2014).

Week 6

[1] Martin Luther, *On Christian Liberty* (reprinted by Fortress Press, 2003). Originally published in 1520.

[2] Article by Marilee Pierce Dunker, 'The Story of White Jade', *World Vision* (2016). Originally published 10 December 2014. Found at [archive.worldvisionmagazine.org/story/story-white-jade] (accessed March 2016).

[3] Article by Tim Stafford, 'Imperfect Instrument', *Christianity Today* (2016). Originally published 24 February 2005. Found at [www.christianitytoday.com/ct/2005/march/19.56.html?start=1] (accessed March 2016).

[4] Pastor Richard Halvorsen, AD 1916–1995.

[5] Bob Pierce, cited in Richard Steams, *The Hole in Our Gospel* (Nashville, TN, USA: World Vision, Inc., 2009).

[6] Mother Teresa, AD 1910–1997.

[7] Material found at [www.niagarafallsinfo.com/history-item.php?entry_id=1357&current_category_id=203] (accessed March 2016).

[8] John Welsey, cited in in Hannah Ward and Jennifer Wild (eds.), *The Lion Christian Quotation Collection* (Oxford, England: Lion Publishing, 1997).

[9] Oliver Goldsmith, AD 1728–1774 (public domain).

[10] Rick Warren, *Better Together Devotional* (Grand Rapids, MI, USA: Zondervan, 2010).

Love With Skin On:
The gift of your journey

This insightful book explains how
Trevor J. Partridge's journey has led
him to understand how the Church
can come alongside people facing
life's challenges. Your journey and
life experiences can become a
valuable gift for another person's
journey. Rediscover the 'paraclesis'
principle and practice of the New
Testament with this model of care for
everyone in the Church and the wider
community.

Author: Trevor J. Partridge
ISBN: 978-1-78259-489-5

For more information or to order,
visit **www.cwr.org.uk/store**
Also available from Christian bookshops.

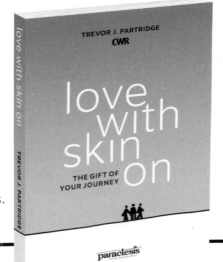

Coming alongside others

Find out more about Paraclesis at
www.paraclesis.org.uk

Journey with God. Every day.

For adults

Every Day with Jesus

The popular daily Bible reading notes by Selwyn Hughes.

Inspiring Women Every Day

Daily insight and encouragement written by women for women.

Life Every Day

Lively Bible notes, with Jeff Lucas' wit and wisdom.

Cover to Cover Every Day

In-depth study of the Bible, book by book. Part of a five-year series.

For children and young adults

Topz (7–11yrs)

An exciting look at the Bible, including fun activities.

YP's (11–15yrs)

Unique, imaginative design and insightful writing.

Mettle (14–18yrs)

Engaging daily notes addressing key issues for teenagers.

 **Printed copies available**    **Large print copies available**    **Daily email available**   **eBooks available**

Courses and seminars
Waverley Abbey College
Publishing and media
Conference facilities

Transforming lives

CWR's vision is to enable people to experience personal transformation through applying God's Word to their lives and relationships.

Our Bible-based training and resources help people around the world to:
• Grow in their walk with God
• Understand and apply Scripture to their lives
• Resource themselves and their church
• Develop pastoral care and counselling skills
• Train for leadership
• Strengthen relationships, marriage and family life and much more.

Our insightful writers provide daily Bible-reading notes and other resources for all ages, and our experienced course designers and presenters have gained an international reputation for excellence and effectiveness.

CWR's Training and Conference Centres in Surrey and East Sussex, England, provide excellent facilities in idyllic settings – ideal for both learning and spiritual refreshment.

CWR Applying God's Word
to everyday life and relationships

CWR, Waverley Abbey House,
Waverley Lane, Farnham,
Surrey GU9 8EP, UK

Telephone: **+44 (0)1252 784700**
Email: info@cwr.org.uk
Website: www.cwr.org.uk

Registered Charity No 294387
Company Registration No 1990308